BY
Esme Hawes

This is a Siena book
Siena is an imprint of Parragon Book Service Ltd

This edition first published by
Parragon Book Service Ltd in 1996

Parragon Book Service Ltd
Unit 13–17 Avonbridge Trading Estate
Atlantic Road, Avonmouth
Bristol BS11 9QD

Produced by Magpie Books Ltd, London

Illustrations courtesy of: Bridgeman Art Library; Hulton Deutsch Collection; Peter Newark's Historical Pictures

ISBN 0 75251 561 6

A copy of the British Library Cataloguing in Publication Data is available from the British Library.

Typeset by Whitelaw & Palmer Ltd, Glasgow

THE PTOLEMYS

Cleopatra, Queen of Egypt, was the heir to a once magnificent kingdom, founded by Alexander the Great but which, at the time of her accession, was in its final stages of decay. By 57 BC Egypt had been ruled by Cleopatra's family, the Ptolemys, for several hundred years, but it was now torn by internecine warfare and was under constant threat from the ever-expanding Roman Empire.

Many years earlier, in 332 BC, Alexander the Great, who was born in Macedonia (now part of Greece), had led his troops out of his native country and on a triumphant campaign of expansionism which extended as far south as Egypt and as far east as India. This incredible enterprise took over ten years to complete and, when Alexander died suddenly in 323 BC, he had not yet had the chance to consolidate his hold on his empire. Though his name was legendary, his imprint was not permanent. Almost as soon as he died, his weak half-brother took over as emperor and the kingdom that Alexander had so laboriously created immediately began to fall apart.

One of Alexander's most important generals was a shrewd military man called Ptolemy, who could see that, very soon, the splintered

Alexander the Great

empire would consist of a series of small and independent states. Wisely, he bargained for the post of governor of one of these – Egypt, which was reputed to be the wealthiest and most self-sufficient kingdom in the entire empire. No other general had the foresight of Ptolemy and, just five months after Alexander's death, he was awarded his prize.

Egypt was a prestigious country. Alexander had been buried there, and it was in Egypt that he had also chosen to found a great city, Alexandria, which had already become one of the most important ports in the Mediterranean. By 305 BC, however, Ptolemy had been proved right and, while the rest of the empire broke up into small, squabbling regions, he had declared himself King of Egypt. He died in 283 BC, and was succeeded by his son, Ptolemy II (whose daughter, Berenice, was subsequently murdered in a struggle for power), whilst Ptolemy IV, his grandson, went on to murder his uncle, his brother and his mother.

No member of the clan, it appeared, could bear to abandon even the slenderest of claims to the throne, and it was Ptolemy VI who started the tradition of consolidating power by marrying his sister, Cleopatra II. On his death, their son inherited the throne as Ptolemy VII, but this child was immediately murdered by Ptolemy VI's brother, who declared himself to be Ptolemy VIII. Cleopatra II instantaneously forgave the new king and married him, only shortly to find herself deposed by one of her own daughters, whom her new husband had raped and then set on the throne in place of her mother. Cleopatra II wasn't to be so easily beaten. She took up arms against her husband who, in revenge, seized one of their own sons as a hostage and had him chopped into small pieces, which he then sent to his mother in a box. Realising, however, that his first wife would soon win in the struggle for power, Ptolemy VIII murdered his stepdaughter-wife and remarried Cleopatra II. The couple buried their differences and had a few more children.

This, therefore, was the family tradition that Cleopatra inherited. By 80 BC her father, Ptolomy XII Auletes, the illegitimate son of Ptolemy IX, was king. He, too, had strengthened his somewhat weak claim to the throne by marrying his sister. The couple had had three daughters, the youngest of whom

Cleopatra by Massimo Stanzione

was born in 69 BC and, though she was to become known as Cleopatra VII, we think of her, quite simply, as 'Cleopatra'.

CHILDHOOD YEARS

In 60 BC Auletes could see that his grip on power was slipping but he could do nothing without the assistance of the rulers of the great Roman Empire. Bravely, he set out on the voyage to Rome in order to confront these, his traditional enemies. In Rome he gained an audience with the three leaders of the empire – Pompey, Crassus and Julius Caesar – and begged them to give him enough money to retain control of his kingdom. Caesar agreed to help Auletes, but only at a staggering rate of interest, which the pharaoh knew would only make him even more dependent on Rome. More disturbingly still, these negotiations had taken quite some time and back in Egypt, in the grand tradition of his family, his two elder daughters were now busily plotting to overthrow their father.

Cleopatra, though not conventionally beautiful, was easily the most intelligent of her father's three daughters, and thus his favourite. She in turn adored her father and, surprisingly, was dismayed to discover how treacherous siblings could be. With her father still abroad, the younger of the two elder sisters had herself declared Berenice IV. Ptolemaic queens could not rule without a male co-regent, however, and so Berenice decided to marry the handsome Prince Archelaus of Asia Minor. Rome, however, would not sanction such a development. Two independent, potentially rich kingdoms could not unite without the consent of their Roman overlords, and Roman troops soon arrived in Egypt to sort matters out. They were led by a brilliant young officer, who directed a remarkable cavalry charge during which Berenice's forces were totally routed, despite their numerical superiority. Auletes returned from Rome and had his second daughter executed. Her husband, Archelaus, had been killed in battle, and Auletes' eldest daughter, who had sided with her rebellious sister, was exiled in disgrace. Cleopatra, still in her teens, was suddenly the heir to the Egyptian throne.

A few days later the young officer who had led the Roman troops to such devastatingly destructive effect arrived in Alexandria with the body of Prince Archelaus. According to custom this prince, who had once offered the Roman hospitality, deserved an honourable burial. The Alexandrians were delighted that the Roman officer demonstrated enough nobility to satisfy this ancient custom, and they were impressed by his request for an audience with Auletes in order to beg for clemency on behalf of the disloyal Egyptian troops against whom he had fought. Cleopatra was now fifteen years old. As heir apparent, she attended the meeting between the king and the handsome foreign officer. He was twenty-nine and his name was Mark Antony. She watched him closely, and found his confidence and his bearing immensely impressive. Antony soon returned to Rome, leaving Auletes firmly on the throne, but his proud image remained firmly imprinted in the young girl's memory.

Just three years later, Auletes died. In his will the eighteen year old Cleopatra was declared queen alongside the elder of her two half-brothers by the king's second marriage. Auletes had also decreed that her co-ruler, the new Ptolemy XIII, at this time ten years old, should one day be the Queen's lover and husband.

CLEOPATRA THE QUEEN

The beauty of the new queen was legendary, even in her own lifetime. In fact, however, it appears from portraits that Cleopatra's physical presence was by no means her most outstanding feature. Even casual observers were most impressed by her charisma, wit and intelligence and, above all, by her firm, cool grasp on the reins of absolute power.

She took great pride in her appearance, spending hours every morning, painting her face and anointing her body in baths of asses' milk. She spent a great deal of time in the library, studying the ancient art of aromatherapy, which had been developing since the days of Queen Hetepheres nearly 3,000 years earlier. She rubbed essential oils into her skin and she was constantly mixing together new perfumes, pressed from the secretions of exotic flowers and animals. She studied the heritage of Ancient Egypt and she encouraged local artisans to make copies of its finest artworks, which she then wore as jewellery or had placed around her palace to remind the Egyptians of their fine and civilised inheritance. Partly because of what was perceived to be her arrogance, however, she was the object of much envy and she grew up in constant fear of assassination. Her rivals hated her, and yet her awestruck people hailed her as a goddess.

But Cleopatra wasn't just a woman of beauty – she was also a shrewd political leader and, with her country heavily in debt to Rome, one of her first important moves was to introduce a number of major financial reforms. She reduced the silver and bronze content of Egypt's coins so that they were no longer worth their face value and she then had this new value imprinted into each coin so that the money dealers could not cheat on their worth. It was an extraordinarily forward-thinking measure, and one that was entirely Cleopatra's invention.

The Egyptians, too, had always felt that their Greek-speaking leaders were constantly discriminating against the local Egyptian-speaking populace. Alexandria, which the Ptolemys used as their capital instead of the traditional Egyptian capital, Memphis, had been created by Alexander (a Greek) for other Greek people, all of whom spoke nothing but Greek and lived an entirely Greek lifestyle. Cleopatra immediately began to remedy this blow to national pride. Though Greek always remained her preferred language, she was the first Ptolemy ever to learn Egyptian and, very shortly, she could speak the native tongue fluently, as well as seven other local languages. For this, quite simple, demonstration of affection for her country, the people adored her.

She knew that she would win their love by becoming more 'Egyptian' and so she studied local religious beliefs and started wearing the vulture headdress of traditional Egyptian mythology. She also began to associate herself with the great goddess Isis and, knowing how much the people revered the ancient cult of sibling intermarriage (according to legend, Isis had married her brother, Osiris), Cleopatra played out a sham wedding with her younger brother.

She started a policy of restoring ancient Egyptian temples, and on many of the redecorated walls she had representations of herself engraved, intertwined with deities. She made regular journeys to Memphis, the ancient capital city, where she attended religious rites and had herself hailed as 'king'. The very holiest of ancient ceremonies was that of *The Apis-Bull* and, when it was time to celebrate this festival, Cleopatra arrived in Memphis in grand style and personally led the ceremonial procession to Thebes in a specially decorated sacred vessel. Although Cleopatra was happy enough to use Ptolemy XIII's name as her brother-husband when it suited her needs, the young boy was entirely excluded from this ritual journey and from the coins which were pressed to commemorate the occasion.

In many ways, however, Cleopatra was just using these displays of wealth to cover up her political problems both at home and abroad. Egypt was the biggest producer of both grain and paper in the whole Mediterranean but it was crippled with debt and almost entirely dependent on its ally, Rome. Her younger brothers by her father's second marriage were constantly threatening to band together and overthrow their half-sister and, though Cleopatra wanted to get rid of them and to consolidate her position as the one true leader, she knew that she could not risk alienating her Roman bankers by concentrating too much power solely in her hands.

Her Roman bankers, meanwhile, had problems of their own. Rome had been totally defeated by the Parthians in the East and Syria was now threatened by these ancient foes of the empire. The new Roman governor in Syria, Marcus Bibulus, sent his two sons to Egypt in order to request extra soldiers to support his troops in their forthcoming battle. The Roman 'peacekeepers' in Egypt loved their new posting, and had no intention of going anywhere that might involve active fighting and potential death. When Bibulus's two sons arrived with their request, the legionaries eliminated the problem by promptly putting them to death. Cleopatra, knowing what trouble this murderous act would create, was outraged. She had the offenders thrown into jail and the bodies of the dead sons transported back to Syria with full state honours. Still only nineteen years old, Cleopatra was in a difficult position, but her sympathetic response to the tragedy pleased very few people. The Roman soldiers resented her for clapping their fellow warriors in chains, while the people of Alexandria thought that she was showing pro-Roman sympathies by sending the bodies back to Syria in state. Cleopatra's position, never easy, had been made even more precarious.

JULIUS CAESAR

In 50 BC the crops failed and famine struck. Ptolemy XIII immediately issued a decree, in the names of both him and his sister-wife, that all available grain should be reserved for Alexandria and that none should be saved for the rest of Egypt. This was guaranteed to upset all of the people who had made up Cleopatra's traditional power base. While Cleopatra began a bitter power struggle with her brother, a civil war started up in Rome. Cleopatra, realising that she was about to lose

Julius Caesar

control, fled to the relative safety of Upper Egypt. Her brother and his entourage remained in Alexandria and seized the reigns of power.

Julius Caesar soon emerged triumphant from the Roman civil war. His vanquished opponent, Pompey, was exiled, and decided to make Alexandria his new home. This development frightened Ptolemy. Everyone knew that the Roman troops were far more effective than the Egyptians and it was a certain bet that Pompey would try to take over the running of the entire kingdom. Ptolemy was still a very young man with little or no real experience of politics. His sister-wife was no longer around to advise him, and the young pharaoh was by nature foolhardy, with an unswerving belief in his own divinity. Pompey reached Alexandria in 48 BC, and found himself, on arrival, being greeted by an official welcome party led by Achillas, an officer sent by Ptolemy. Achillas accompanied Pompey ashore, paid him the usual compliments and then, obeying Ptolemy's strict instructions, stabbed the Roman to death. Cleopatra, learning the terrible news, immediately fled northwards to Ashkelon, a Philistine city in Roman-occupied Palestine, and thereby dissociated herself from the act of treachery. Just four days later Caesar, predictably, landed in Egypt.

He was greeted by one of Ptolemy's tutors, who offered him Pompey's severed head on a tray, thinking that this would please the Roman. Caesar was not impressed. Egypt owed him money; Egypt had murdered a noble man; and Egypt was clearly being run by an idiot. Caesar was also a man of his

Apollodorus delivers the carpet to Caesar in the 1963 film, *Cleopatra*

word. He had promised his former friend, Auletes, that he would maintain both Cleopatra and her brother on the throne, a condition that he fully intended to fulfil. Cleopatra had already anticipated this and wrote to Caesar telling him her whereabouts. Caesar sent for the exiled queen, but the harbour at Alexandria was blocked by Ptolemy's guards and Cleopatra knew that she could never hope to get past these men without some form of subterfuge.

Dressed as a simple fisherman, she set out to sea in a tiny dinghy with just one companion, a eunuch called Apollodorus. Dragging their nets behind them, the pair cheerfully sailed into the great harbour at Alexandria and then right past Ptolemy's ever-watchful guards. They landed without difficulty, then quickly changed their disguises. Apollodorus became a carpet dealer, and soon he was to be seen walking through the streets of Alexandria with a huge oriental rug slung over his muscular shoulder. He marched straight into the great hall of the magnificent palace, where he knew that Caesar would be sitting in state. Walking up to the dictator, he placed the rug down on the floor before Caesar's feet and then, with a single flourish, he took out a dagger and cut through the leather thong with which the rolled-up carpet was bound. Slowly the carpet unfurled and, before Caesar's eyes, the lovely Cleopatra emerged from its centre, scantily clad in transparent oriental costume. Smoothing herself down, she stood up and, staring the mighty Roman general straight in the eye, she smiled.

Caesar's heart was ablaze. He listened in silence as Cleopatra recounted her tale of indignity and, fascinated by her initiative, intelligence and courage, he fell madly, passionately in love. In one fell swoop, Ptolemy's position was undermined and there was nothing the Egyptian king could do. Caesar's troops were far superior to his own and the majority of Egyptians were still loyal to his sister. Politely but firmly, Caesar asked Ptolemy to remove himself to a separate wing of the palace, and the pharaoh could not disobey.

Caesar, more than twice the age of his new consort, moved into the king's old quarters and took Cleopatra with him, disporting himself like an adolescent boy. He was totally bowled over by the Queen's outstanding virtues, and she, in turn, felt that for once in her life she had met her intellectual and spiritual equal. They conversed in both Latin and Greek, and Caesar had never met a woman with such independence of spirit, charm and all-embracing knowledge. All those solitary days in the library had paid off for Cleopatra, and contemporary reports state that it was not her physical attributes which assailed Caesar's senses (though neither was it Caesar's which assailed hers), but the immense personality, strength of character and thoughtfulness which poured forth with every word she uttered. 'It was a delight merely to hear the sound of her voice', wrote one scholar and Caesar, delighted, couldn't hear it enough. The pair were never apart, and they flaunted their mutual adoration for all to see. The palace was stunned by this turn of events, and so was Ptolemy. Quite apart from the personal snub to him, still officially her brother-husband, Caesar was the sworn enemy of the popular imagination. Here was the love-affair of private dreams and public nightmares.

Troops began to gather behind Achillas, who had become a figurehead for resistance since the day he murdered Pompey. Caesar heard the news and urged the young Ptolemy to send envoys of peace to his former messenger and to tell him to lay down his arms. Ptolemy, now living under the same roof as Caesar, could hardly refuse. He sent some men to talk to Achillas, but they were murdered on their arrival. Caesar began to keep a close watch on young Ptolemy. He had just overcome a bloody civil war at home and he could recognise the signs of growing dissent. Cleopatra, meanwhile, stuck closely to Caesar's side and bided her time. Rival soldiers began to skirmish regularly outside the palace walls and Caesar took to patrolling with his troops during the day, while sending reports of his total mastery of the situation back to Rome. Since he already had a wife in his home city, however, he neglected to mention his growing personal attachment to the area.

Arsinoe, Ptolemy's sister, had always been excluded from power, and though just seventeen years old, she decided that the time was ripe for her to take control of her destiny. One night she slipped out of the palace and went to join Achillas, and to lend him her support. A large number of Alexandrians, fed up with Cleopatra's frolickings with an enemy more than twice her age, were thrilled to have a potential new leader behind whom to throw their weight. Arsinoe was declared the true Queen of Egypt and Achillas's troops began to encircle the palace. Caesar had to act quickly. He strengthened the fortifications, set fire to as many of Achillas's ships as he could locate and, in his own ships, carried a detachment of soldiers to the Pharos or lighthouse, from which any boats entering or leaving the harbour could be observed. This was, effectively, the beginning of the Alexandrian War.

The Roman general, pinned down on the isthmus on which the lighthouse stood, was surrounded. Confusion ensued and Caesar ran from the lighthouse to his ship, closely pursued by the enemy soldiers, who started boarding the vessel after him. Heavily armoured, he jumped overboard and was shot at with arrows while he swam as fast as he could to one of the other ships, anchored further out to sea. Cleopatra, watching events from the palace window, feared for both her lover's safety and, more immediately, her own life. She saw Caesar's ship sink, and then she saw his soldiers, desperately keen to return to battle and tear Achillas's men to pieces. Caesar restrained them, realising that it was now best to retreat and regroup, particularly because he had one new trump card up his sleeve – on the boat with him was young Ptolemy, whom he had taken hostage and who was now sitting on deck, crying and begging for mercy.

It was stalemate. The Alexandrians sent to Caesar and asked him to release their king. The Roman said he would grant the snivelling juvenile his life, if only he would promise to keep good faith with Rome in future. Ptolemy shed tears of gratitude and kissed Caesar's hands. As soon as he was ashore and Caesar's troops had disembarked, Ptolemy declared war.

Caesar and Cleopatra on the Nile

Caesar sailed on to an eastern garrison town, Pelusium, where he knew that reinforcements were waiting for him. Ptolemy followed him. After several minor skirmishes, Caesar realised that Ptolemy didn't know the first thing about warfare and that he had left his troops with their rear unguarded. Caesar bombarded this gap in the defence and, taking Ptolemy's forces by storm, cut straight through them. The king fled in a partially holed ship which soon capsized. Within a few minutes, Ptolemy was drowned.

Caesar returned to Alexandria as a conquering hero. Cleopatra, who was now pregnant, was delighted to see the triumphant return of her child's father, even though the cost to Egypt was its full annexation by Rome. Caesar set her back on the throne with her remaining half-brother, Ptolemy XIV, at her side. He then collected his debts and, in 47 BC, took Cleopatra on a cruise up the Nile. The vessel in which they sailed was a floating palace of love. Made from the cedars of Lebanon and Cyprus, it was impressively decorated and equipped with all manner of luxury goods. This wasn't just a tribute to the mother of his child, however. It was also a public relations exercise for a man who never forgot about power.

Cleopatra was once more secure on the throne, but Caesar was showing her subjects that she had not forgotten the Egyptian-speaking people of the South. He, too, took to wearing local costume, and the couple went to the great temple of Luxor where they offered incense and libations to the chief Egyptian gods. Cleopatra was still only twenty-two. She wore transparent robes of linen and soft, pastel silk, which had been brought to her by merchants from remote China. Adoring locals ran along the banks of the river to catch a glimpse of their magical leaders, and Cleopatra felt secure.

Eventually they came back to the capital. Caesar had been away from Rome for almost a year and he knew that he would soon have to return there. To commemorate his visit, Cleopatra planned a great architectural monument on the seafront at Alexandria which was to be called the Caesareum and which, when completed, was a perfect blend of both Egyptian and Greek influences. It was the tallest building in the harbour and its façade was fronted by two obelisks.

Caesar and his wife had only ever had one child, a daughter called Julia who was now in

Cleopatra and Caesarion, shown on a relief at Dendera

her mid-thirties. Caesar's great-nephew and adopted son, Octavian, therefore had his sights firmly set on becoming his uncle's heir, and when Cleopatra gave birth to a son in 47 BC, Octavian absolutely refused to acknowledge the boy as Caesar's child. Though there can be little dispute that Caesarion (little Caesar) was the dictator's child, there was, however, no desire in Rome for his birth to become public knowledge. In any event, Caesar had more immediate problems to resolve since he, too, was fighting an internal battle for control of Rome and its empire.

In Egypt, Cleopatra worked hard to regain absolute power. Much of the internal spirit of resistance had been shattered by the rebels' failure in the Alexandrian War, and she no longer had tedious daily domestic battles in the palace. By 46 BC she felt that she was in a strong enough position at home to make a trip to visit Caesar abroad. The queen didn't want her young half-brother seizing power while she was away, however, so she took Ptolemy XIV with her as well as her baby son and a number of courtiers. In Rome, Caesar installed the party in one of his own palaces, where Cleopatra maintained a splendid lifestyle which rather annoyed both the Senate and Caesar's wife, Calpurnia, who thought that their dictator had fallen for an extravagant upstart.

Neither wife nor mistress prevented Caesar from launching a campaign against Mauretania that year and, whilst there, seducing Eunoe, the wife of Bogud, the country's vanquished king. On his triumphant return to Rome, however, he made it clear that Cleopatra was still his favourite consort. He built the Forum Julium, a magnificent building with a temple in the middle of it and, in the very centre of this temple, he took the unprecedented step of placing a golden statue, not of his wife, but of Cleopatra – a foreign ruler. Loving though this gesture may have been, it merely served further to antagonise both Caesar's family and the Senate.

Still, they too were benefiting from the new alliance. Such new-fangled ideas as the 365-day calendar and the concept of the leap year were innovations that Cleopatra had brought with her from Egypt, and she also spent time teaching the Romans about irrigation as well as the efficient organisation of libraries and archives.

In 45 BC Caesar made his will. There could be

no question of his naming an illegitimate, foreign child as his heir. Instead he declared Octavian, his sister Julia's grandson, as the man who would succeed him. Cleopatra could not have been surprised by this, but both she and Caesar were soon to be tragically surprised by the depth of ill feeling that had grown up against the dictator himself.

The Romans had grown heartily sick of being taxed heavily in order to fund what they thought of as Caesar's private battles, and, besides, he seemed to have become more and more despotic and tyrannical. He had the month of Quintilis renamed Julius (or July) after him, and his statue was borne in processions like that of a God. 'How long are we going to let this man play the king?', asked members of the Senate, and though Mark Antony crowned him 'dictator for life'

Cleopatra's Needle, Alexandria by David Roberts

in 44 BC, his power had grown too great for the senators to endure.

On the 'Ides' of March (8 March) 44 BC, Julius Caesar stood up in the Senate to make a straightforward political speech and was brutally and viciously stabbed to death by over fifty of the other senators. Bleeding from every part of his body, Caesar fell dead at the feet of the statue of Pompey. Octavian returned from abroad and declared himself 'Caesar'. Cleopatra knew that she must leave the country straight away. On the way back to Egypt, Ptolemy mysteriously died of poisoning, aged fifteen. After the party returned to Alexandria, Caesarion was later named Ptolemy XV and declared joint king of Egypt with his mother. Cleopatra knew that Octavian Caesar would now have his sights firmly set on Egypt and that her son would be a prime target. She could do little but strengthen their position against the inevitable attack.

Mark Antony's Oration by George Robertson

MARK ANTONY

Mark Antony had been Caesar's favourite officer. Though he must have been bitterly disappointed not to be mentioned in Caesar's will, this didn't detract from his unswerving devotion to his former mentor. It was Antony who delivered Caesar's funeral oration, beginning his speech, according to Shakespeare, with the immortal phrase 'Friends, Romans, Countrymen'. Brutus and Cassius, the two leaders of the murderous assault, fled abroad, from where they sent a message to Cleopatra, asking for troops to assist them in the defeat of Octavian's troops. Despite Octavian's antagonism, Cleopatra could not believe that the murderers of her son's father could ask for her assistance. Instead of helping the traitors, she sent reinforcements to defeat them and, though this ploy worked, her military strength was weakened and Cassius grew to hate her and to desire her downfall.

Cleopatra's half-sister, Arsinoe, was still alive and waiting for another chance at power. Naturally she joined forces with Cassius. In Rome, Antony and Octavian became the effective joint rulers of the empire, and Cleopatra set sail in a fleet of boats to assist Antony in a new fight against Cassius. Almost immediately a storm blew up and her boats were shattered. Cleopatra returned home but

Antony, though fighting alone, was completely victorious in battle. Brutus and Cassius did the honourable thing and committed suicide, and Octavian and Antony then divided the Roman world between them. Octavian took the west, Antony the east, and a new era had begun.

The Antonine family, though plebeian in origin, had for generations belonged to the highest levels of the ruling class. Mark Antony's grandfather, an orator who specialised in pathos, had been killed in battle, and his father had stayed out of politics and squandered a great deal of the family wealth on drink and gambling. He became a magistrate and used his new position to gain command of the office in charge of subduing the pirates who plagued the Mediterranean. Under cover of this post he went to Sicily,

Richard Burton as Antony in the 1963 film

where he was ambushed by pirates and killed. Antony, born around 83 BC, was ten years old at the time and his father's squalid death was a heavy blow to his images of manhood. His mother, Julia, who was distantly related to Caesar, soon remarried and she watched Antony grow up to be more and more like his father, handsome, energetic and impulsive, but with a reputation for excess in all things. He ran up huge debts as well as making hundreds of female conquests, and Caesar, though he loved him as a father, realised that Antony needed to learn self-discipline.

Caesar sent Antony to Greece where the young soldier developed a love of all things Hellenic which was to stay with him throughout his life. He threw himself into the study of ancient Greek disciplines like military strategy and athletics, but though he

Cleopatra disembarking at Taise by Claude Lorrain

was a talented sportsman, he still had a tendency to over-indulge. He was twenty-nine when he first distinguished himself in battle, and none of the parties involved ever forgot his noble assistance to Auletes, Cleopatra's father all those years earlier. He had shown at the time that he was an honourable man – brave in battle and generous in victory.

Bearded and laddish, Antony didn't set himself above his soldiers, like most of the other leaders, but ate and drank in their tents with them and won both their approval and their hearts. Though Caesar had left him nothing in his will, everyone knew that this was merely a matter of convenience and that Antony was far superior to Octavian in every way. He was better-looking, a more distinguished soldier, and infinitely more popular with the people. It is significant, therefore, that Antony chose to govern the eastern section of the empire. He knew that Caesar had particularly wished to renew his campaign against Parthia before he died, and Antony dearly wanted to follow in his mentor's thwarted footsteps and, in some way, to avenge his memory.

ANTONY AND CLEOPATRA

Antony sailed to Asia Minor, where he undertook a hugely successful military campaign in the course of which he became rather wealthy. His ultimate aim was the conquest of Persia, but he realised straight away that the gateway to victory in the whole Parthian area (which nowadays includes most of the Middle East) was Egypt. And Egypt *was* Cleopatra.

Antony sent for Cleopatra to meet him at Tarsus, in the south-east corner of Asia Minor. Cleopatra was a proud woman, however, and didn't answer to the beck and call of a mere co-ruler of Rome. She bided her time, letting weeks pass. When she eventually set out northwards, she travelled in such spectacular style that her journey became the most talked about in the ancient world. Plutarch describes her boat, which was entirely covered in gold. Its sails were purple and its oars silver. An orchestra of flutes, viols and zithers stood on the deck, playing music, while Cleopatra sat swathed in golden tissue, dressed up as Venus, the goddess of love. Two blond pageboys stood on either side of her, dressed as Cupids, fanning her head, and they, in turn, were surrounded by women dressed as mermaids. The entire boat was drenched in perfume, and hundreds of people ran along the shore, calling out to their queen and falling to the ground in adoration.

Eventually, Cleopatra landed at Tarsus and Antony sent for her to dine with him. Does the mountain go to Muhammad? Cleopatra replied that, rather, he should come to her. Never before had a woman said 'no' to Antony, and never before had he felt that a woman was worthy of his respect. He arrived and he was stunned. Boarding the barge, he stood amazed by the sumptuous fare served up before him, only to be repeatedly astonished by the plethora of courses appearing in front of him, each one more fabulous and inventive than the last. An apparently infinite number of flaming torches miraculously lit every impressive element of Cleopatra's extravaganza and, gazing at her in the magical firelight, Antony fell totally, utterly and hopelessly in love. It was a love that would last a lifetime.

The impossibly perfect couple were immediately associated with divine figures in the minds of the many people who saw them together. That Bacchus and Venus should become inseparable lovers was only logical, and Antony and Cleopatra were the closest thing to gods that most people could ever hope to see. They were clearly destined for each other, but politics had its part to play also. 'Had Cleopatra's ships really set out to sea to help Antony in the battle after Caesar's death,' he asked, 'or was this just a convenient tale?' 'Was Antony going to love Cleopatra and then leave her for some other symbol of power, like her half-sister, Arsinoe?' demanded the queen. Antony threw caution to the wind and committed himself totally to Cleopatra's cause

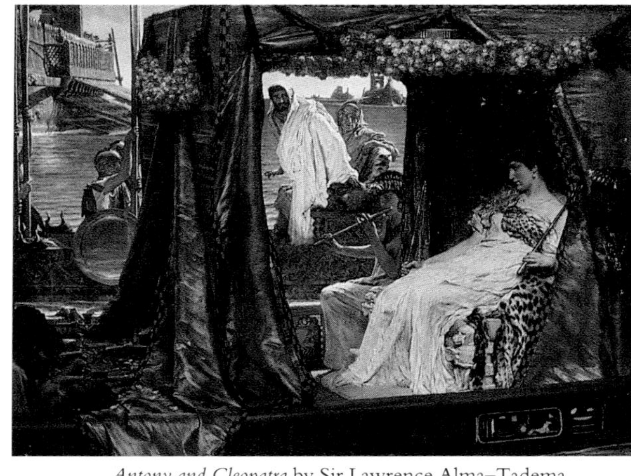

Antony and Cleopatra by Sir Lawrence Alma–Tadema

– he sent for Arsinoe and then had her executed. He would never tolerate a force that could destabilise either himself, his country or his love.

The pair returned to Egypt in December 41 BC and once there, Antony tactfully stood by Cleopatra's side as a welcome visitor, rather than a conquering Roman warrior. They spent the winter together, organising parties and generally celebrating their love. They were happy, and they wanted everyone else to be happy, too. Plutarch records that at one particular dinner eight boars were roasted for just twelve people. Cleopatra had new coins pressed on which her image was modified to suit her new role. Her hair was curlier and more sophisticated than it used to be and her dresses were much grander. She wore pearls from India, though these had only ever been popular in Rome, and she had her palace redecorated. Now the couple were surrounded by marble walls with gilded ceilings, alabaster floors and doors inlaid with ebony and ivory. Their furniture was embedded with precious stones, their cups and goblets were made of jasper, their tableware was solid silver and gold.

Cleopatra loved knowledge and Antony loved Cleopatra. The pair spent long hours in the Alexandria Museum and in the famous Library, which was the best in the world. Both of these institutions, complete with permanent research staff and archivists, were located within the palace walls and Cleopatra constantly conversed with the many scholars who came to visit. She studied the history of art and architecture and Antony studied with her. But he had his own interests, too, and

Antony and Cleopatra by G. Lerouisse

Cleopatra accompanied him on hunting and fishing trips, during which they talked about his long-cherished plan to return to Parthia, and thereby strengthen his position (and hers) within the Roman Empire.

Eventually, though with Cleopatra's blessing, Antony sailed away to conquer the East. Almost as soon as he left, however, he received news from Rome that his wife, Fulvia, and his brother had led an unsuccessful revolt against Octavian and had had to flee Italy. Everyone in Rome had heard about Antony's affair with Cleopatra and almost everyone disapproved. There was little that Antony could do about Parthia now – he had to return to deal with his pressing domestic problems. Back in Italy in 40 BC, he met Octavian and blamed all of his problems on his faithless wife, Fulvia. Octavian was indulgent and, fortunately, Fulvia was no longer around to defend herself, for she died suddenly of natural causes. This was convenient for Octavian, since his beautiful sister, Octavia, had recently been widowed and he wished to bind Antony to himself with new, family ties.

Antony never denied his relationship with Cleopatra, but everyone in Rome conspired to keep him in his home city and to throw him into the arms of Octavia. Technically she was too recently widowed to be married again but no one really cared and, just a few months later, Antony did as he was told. The pair went to Greece, where Octavia had a baby girl, Antonia, and they set up a home which included Antyllus, Antony's son and heir by his first wife, Fulvia.

Three whole winters passed and Antony relinquished the Parthian campaign to a very able general called Ventidius. Outright victory was, in fact, very close when Ventidius tactfully decided to return to Rome, since he had no wish to steal the limelight from Antony. This proved to be unfortunate because, as things turned out, Rome would never again be so close to conquering the east.

Octavia in 37 BC was now pregnant with Antony's second daughter, and Octavian was beginning to be fearful of Antony's constant victories and his increasing hold on power. In a spirit of harmony, the couple sailed back to Italy, where Octavia acted as peacemaker between her husband and her brother and Antony promised to give Octavian more ships, while Octavian promised to give

Antony extra footsoldiers. Everything on the domestic front now appeared to be relatively peaceful and so, as soon as he was able, Antony told Octavia that he planned to renew his Parthian campaign. She pleaded with her husband to stay in Italy but, though he did not mention this, it was almost three years since he had seen the love of his life and he could no longer bear the pain of absence.

Voyaging straight to Alexandria would have been a little tactless, so Antony went to North Syria, from where he sent for the Egyptian queen. Cleopatra rushed to join him and, there, in the city of Antioch in 37 BC, they were 'married'. Antony gave Cleopatra land in Phoenicia, Syria and Cyprus. As soon as the Romans heard this, they bitterly resented what they saw as the reconstruction of the old Ptolemaic Empire and the wild, extravagant hussy who had ensnared their leader. To top it all, they then heard that Cleopatra had given birth to twins – a son called Alexander Helios (the sun) and a daughter called Cleopatra Selene (the moon). Antony and Cleopatra were in heaven.

THE PARTHIAN CAMPAIGN

Cleopatra returned to Egypt and Antony journeyed on to Armenia. The Roman army now had 50,000 men but Antony was handicapped by his overwhelming desire to return to his beloved. Instead of waiting for spring and giving his men time to rest and recover from their journey, he rushed them forwards as fast as they could go, and in very poor weather conditions. This haste caused him to make a catastrophic mistake. Antony and his soldiers arrived at the great city of Media long before the 300 carts which were carrying the vital siege equipment necessary to conquer it. They were stranded outside the city with no siege train and, therefore, no siege engines or battering rams to break down its walls and gates. The element of surprise had been utterly lost and there was nothing that the men could do but start scaling the walls of the city without any specialised equipment. They were sitting targets. While they were picked off one by one, the king of Media sent his army on a roundabout route out of the city and caught the rest of the besiegers by surprise from behind. Ten thousand Roman legionaries and auxiliaries were wiped out in one day, and Antony hastily withdrew before incurring further losses.

Though never much of a politician, Antony had always been a brave leader of men. He decided to counter-attack, and in one great charge he did, indeed, send the Parthians flying in disarray. But the pyrrhic victory was too little, too late. The Romans had won this particular battle, but they had lost more men than they had killed and now they were left isolated and under strength in the farthest corner of the empire. Antony was in his late forties and his heart and mind were elsewhere. His warm-hearted, passionate nature was perfect for active warfare, but he could never command the kind of calculated judgement and military resolve that had made Caesar so successful. The rest of his Parthian campaign was a tale of death, disease and famine. Though the troops still loved him, they were stuck in a strange land and beginning to starve. In misery and remorse Antony wandered amongst his soldiers, visiting the sick and comforting the dying. Food had run out and the men ate herbs and roots, which caused dysentery to spread. With 25,000 men collapsing at his feet, Antony withdrew to Armenia in anger and despair, were he sent for the king of Armenia and, as poor recompense, had him locked in chains.

It was now deepest midwinter. The weary legionaries trudged through the snow, loyal to the bitter end. Sorrowfully, Antony sent for Cleopatra, who took a long time to arrive due to the harsh conditions. Eventually, she found Antony, half-drunk, in the harbour near Sidon, standing on the shoreline and watching out for her boat to arrive, while clutching an empty bottle. Cleopatra had brought food, money and clothing with her, but her heart sank. She could see now why

Caesar had chosen Octavian as his successor – the new Caesar might be a ruthless, cold-hearted automaton, but these very qualities gave him strength of purpose and overwhelming ambition. No love could ever have shaken Octavian's resolve. Cleopatra knew that her tender-hearted consort would never now be able to help her realise her dream of an all-powerful Egyptian kingdom, but still she remained loyal. Octavia was also loyal to her husband. She wrote to Antony offering assistance, and he wrote back asking her to send reinforcements. Cleopatra realised that this was probably Antony's last chance for survival and so, tactfully, she pretended to be ill, and hid. Still the troops did not arrive. Antony returned to Alexandria. Octavian, resentful of Antony's treatment of his sister, reported to the Senate that Antony was a defeated man who had run from the field of battle in order to spend time with a woman, and though Antony tried to regain some prestige by sacking Armenia, everyone knew that it was a small, defenceless country. No one was fooled or impressed.

Slowly, Cleopatra made her way back to Alexandria with as much ceremony as she could muster. In Judaea she met Herod who did not like her. But she was still the beautiful leader of Egypt, and the Judaean king offered her gifts and accompanied her for some of the way back to Egypt. A number of people reported that he made sexual advances towards her and that she rejected him mercilessly, thus creating yet another humbled enemy keen to bring about her downfall.

In 35 BC, Antony also returned to Alexandria

from Armenia, and immediately tried to drum up support by organising a display of immense extravagance which he called the 'Donations'. Antony and Cleopatra summoned the people to the grand arena, where the couple sat on golden thrones raised on a silver dais. Antony, in a direct challenge to Octavian, called out to the people that Cleopatra had been Caesar's wife and that Caesarion was Caesar's son and real heir. Cleopatra was dressed as Isis and Antony as Osiris and their divine marriage was proclaimed. Beneath them sat Caesarion and their own children. Antony declared Cleopatra to be 'Queen of Kings' and Caesarion 'King of Kings'. Alexander, their son, now six years old, was dressed as the Parthian king whilst his twin sister became Queen of Libya and their small brother Ptolemy Philadelphus (who had been born in 37 BC), was made overlord of the Euphrates.

Antony had a commemorative coin pressed, which had the legend 'Armenia conquered' on one side and 'Cleopatra, Queen of Kings' on the other. Rome shuddered in horror. It seemed that Antony had gone mad with love and that he was now giving away his whole empire to the Egyptian witch.

The Romans were sick of civil wars. Octavian therefore declared a united Italy, which he now set about reconstructing. He wasn't terribly bothered about the wild proclamations from Alexandra, since Antony was clearly a spent force suffering from strange, demented delusions, but he was concerned at Cleopatra's apparently growing ambition. Octavian wanted to rule the world, and he was not going to let Cleopatra get in his way. It was looking increasingly inevitable that he would be forced to make a trip to

A coin of Cleopatra

Egypt and there confront the apparently growing dissent from Roman control. Antony confirmed this by sending many of the plundered goods from Armenia straight back to Alexandria, where it appeared that he intended to live permanently.

Antony and Cleopatra knew that Octavian would soon arrive. They mobilised a great fleet and, although Antony's remaining soldiers did not really want to fight on behalf of an Egyptian queen, they realised that she was now paying their wages and that their general was utterly committed to her cause. The couple set sail with their fleet for Athens, where Cleopatra was greeted as a descendant of local kings. From there, Antony sent word to Rome that Octavia was his wife no longer and that she should be expelled from the family home with all her children. The

Romans pitied Octavia, but they also pitied Antony.

Though Octavian was surprised by his enemies' active initiative, he also realised that Antony would be unwilling to fight unless it should become absolutely necessary. Octavian gathered a small fleet and in 31 BC set sail across the Adriatic. Antony could have taken him by surprise at sea, where he stood a better chance of success, but hesitancy had sunk in and, fatally, he chose to wait. The troops finally met at Actium on the east coast of Greece.

Antony remained profoundly unhappy about giving his men an order to fight against other Roman troops; thus, by the time he did so, Octavian's fleet was already in the harbour and fully protected. Meanwhile other Roman troops had cut off Antony's grain supplies, so that there was little he could now do save retreat to dry land where he, in turn, hoped to cut off Octavian's supply of fresh water. But Antony's cavalry were weary and deeply uneasy about fighting their fellow Romans. Desertions began, and Antony suddenly found himself the besieged party. The wind changed and both sides rushed to their ships and to sea, desperate to take advantage of the new conditions. Two-thirds of Antony's fleet realised that defeat was inevitable, however, and immediately switched sides. He was left with just a few diehard supporters, and saw that the situation was hopeless. Sending a special, secret signal to Cleopatra, who was waiting out at sea, he rowed out to join her and then sat in her boat with his head in his hands, weeping like a broken man. Cleopatra headed home.

Cameo commemorating the Battle of Actium

Sailing back to Alexandria, Cleopatra garlanded her remaining ships as if they had been victorious, but she knew that her position was now untenable. While Antony remained in a state of torpor, lifeless and crushed, Octavian would defeat her country – and he would never allow such a figurehead as Cleopatra to remain on the throne. Her best bet, at this stage, was to show as little resistance as possible; Octavian then might just allow her children to be named as her successors. There seemed little point in increasing the suffering of her people by more unnecessary bloodshed and so Cleopatra forbade the Egyptians to fight.

Octavian finally arrived in the summer of 30 BC. He pitched his camp outside Alexandria and, on Cleopatra's fortieth birthday, Antony organised one last cavalry charge. She, meanwhile, filled her own tomb with treasures and awaited the worst. Antony sent word to Octavian that he would fight him to the death, man to man, but Octavian replied that Antony would shortly find many other ways to die.

In the morning Antony went up to the hills to watch his fleet sail out to sea, and to the attack. Staring helplessly, he saw his men sail their ships alongside Octavian's and then, instead of attacking, salute the enemy troops, who saluted back. The shock was too much for Antony. Crazed and beside himself, he assumed that Cleopatra had betrayed him by making a deal with Octavian. Though this was not the case, Cleopatra was afraid of her mad lover's wrath and, locking herself inside her tomb, sent word that she was dead.

Antony was in despair. A noble Roman

The Death of Antony and Cleopatra by Alessandro Turchi

would have killed himself, but he had become a shadow of his former self. Falling to his knees, he begged his assistant, Eros, to do the dreadful deed. Eros drew his sword but, instead of Antony, he stabbed himself. Humbled by his assistant's true nobility of spirit, Antony fell upon his own sword in shame, but he did not die. From the shelter of her tomb, Cleopatra heard that he was still alive. She commanded her two women servants to haul Antony's bleeding body across the palace and into her hiding place, where she took Antony into her arms. With his dying words, he urged her to plead with Octavian for her own safety.

But Cleopatra was a queen, and she knew that this could never be. Just seconds later Antony died in her arms, and in her grief Cleopatra tore out her hair and beat her breast. Octavian entered Alexandria without encountering any resistance and, not wishing her to become a martyr, rapidly gave orders for his men to fetch the queen alive. Leaving a note that her children should succeed her, Cleopatra stabbed herself only moments before the arrival of the Roman troops. Rushing into her tomb, they snatched the dagger out of her hands, then locked her in the chamber while they plundered her palace.

Octavian wanted the Egyptian people to see their queen defeated and in chains. Soon he arrived at the palace and marched into her chamber, demanding to know the whereabouts of all her hidden treasures, but Cleopatra, though feverish from self-inflicted stab wounds, suddenly rose up, proud to the last, and punched him in the face. Octavian laughed and left the room.

The Death of Cleopatra by Reginald Arthur

Cleopatra knew that Octavian would exile her and then have her murdered abroad. She wanted to die amongst her own people, and she wanted to be buried near the man she loved. Placing flowers on her tomb, she dressed for dinner and then sent for a specially prepared basket of figs to be brought in and placed before her at the table. She barred all the doors to the chamber, and then pulled a poisonous asp out from amongst the figs where it had been hidden. Taking the asp in her hands, Cleopatra said goodbye to the world and then clasped the snake to her heart.

Octavian quickly got wind of what had happened and ran to the tomb, but he was too late. Cleopatra was already dead, lying on a golden couch and dressed like a monarch, with both of her women servants lying dead at her feet. Despite himself, Octavian recognised that Cleopatra had been a true queen amongst women. Just a few days later he had Caesarion, her son by Julius Caesar, murdered, and then he returned home and did the same to Antony's son and heir from his marriage to Fulvia. Octavian had himself declared pharaoh, and Egypt became a province of the Roman Empire. Rome, which now became Egypt's ruler in every respect, had conquered an entire dynasty. Cleopatra was, therefore, the very last Ptolemy ever to reign in Egypt.

A Templar Book

Produced by The Templar Company plc,
Pippbrook Mill, London Road, Dorking, Surrey RH4 1JE, Great Britain.

This edition produced for Parragon Books,
Unit 13-17, Avonbridge Trading Estate, Atlantic Road, Avonmouth, Bristol BS11 9QD

This book contains material first published as
The Adventures of the Toy Ship in Enid Blyton's Sunny Stories
and Sunny Stories between 1926 and 1953.

Illustrated by Alison Winfield

Printed and bound in Italy

ISBN 1 85813 528 1

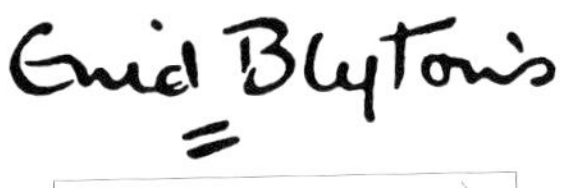

POCKET LIBRARY

THE ADVENTURES OF THE TOY SHIP

Illustrated by Alison Winfield

PARRAGON

Mary and Timothy had a little ship. It had a fine blue sail, and its name *Lucy Ann* was painted on the side. The children often took it down to the stream to sail it, and it floated beautifully. It didn't turn over on its side as so many toy boats do – it sailed upright, just like a proper boat.

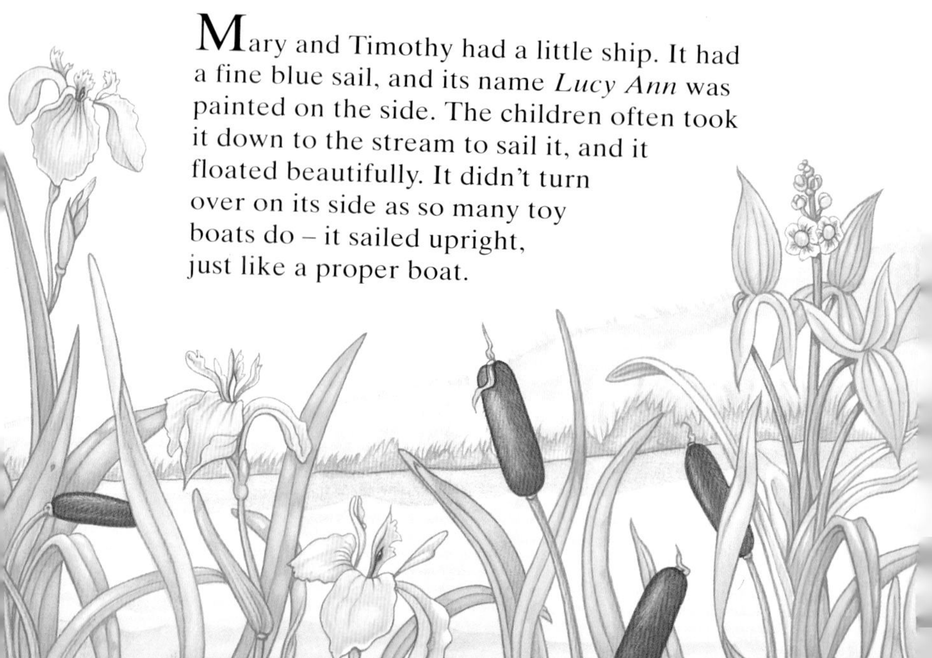

One day when Mary and Timothy were sailing the *Lucy Ann*, the string broke.

Oh dear! Down the stream it floated, faster and faster, and the children ran after it. But the little boat kept to the middle of the stream and, no matter how they tried, the children could not reach it.

At last they could no longer run by the stream, for someone's big garden ran right down to the edge of the water, and a fence stood in their way. Very sad, the children watched as the *Lucy Ann* disappeared around a bend in the stream. They went back home, afraid that their ship would feel very lost without them.

So it did. The little ship tried its hardest to go back, but the stream took it along too fast. On and on it went until at last it came to rest beside a mossy bank. Its prow stuck into the soft earth and there it stayed. The little ship could move neither backwards nor forwards.

Night came, and the ship was astonished to see the moon in the sky, for before it had always spent the night in the toy cupboard. It did not know that there were such things as moon or stars. It stared up at the big silver moon and thought it was very beautiful.

Then suddenly, through the silence of the night there came the sound of singing. On the opposite side of the stream, the little ship was surprised to see a great many twinkling lights, like tiny Japanese lanterns, shining in rainbow colours through the darkness.

It heard a lot of little voices, and saw a great number of fairy folk, all most excited. They were dressed in beautiful costumes – rose petal waistcoats edged with diamond dewdrops, daffodil skirts and bluebell waistcoats.

Then, as the little boat watched in amazement, a ring of toadstools sprang up, and the pixies laid little white cloths on them for tables. They set out plates and glasses, and tiny knives and forks. Then they put out some tiny golden chairs for a group of pixies who carried musical instruments.

These must be the fairy folk that Mary and Timothy sometimes talked about, thought the ship to itself. Then it saw a small boat, smaller than itself, on the opposite side of the stream, and a pixie-man got into it.

Quite nearby, on the top of its own mossy bank, the ship saw more fairy folk. They had with them all sorts of good things to eat! Honey cakes, flower biscuits, blue jellies with pink ice cream on the top, lemonade made of dew, special blancmanges in the shape of birds and animals, and many other good things.

They carried these goodies in woven baskets and on silver dishes. They were waiting for the other little boat to fetch them across the stream, so that they might lay out their food on the ring of toadstool tables.

"Hey! Little boat, come and fetch us!" they cried to the boat on the other side. The pixie-man in it began to row across. But suddenly a great fish popped up its head and made such a large wave that the pixie boat was filled with water and sank!

Oh, what a noise there was! How all the little folk shouted and cried in fear, when they saw their boat sink, and the pixie-man in the water!

"Oh, no! The boat's sunk! Oh, look at the boatman, is he safe? Oh, what shall we do now! We haven't another boat and all our lovely food is on the other side of the stream!"

Listening in dismay, the *Lucy Ann* suddenly had a grand idea! It could take the pixies to the other side, with all their baskets and dishes! So it spoke up in its funny, watery voice. How all the fairy folk jumped when they heard it! One little pixie was so surprised that she dropped the dish she was carrying, and spilt blue jelly all over the grass.

"I will take you across the stream, if you know how to sail me," said the little ship. "Don't be frightened. I am only a toy ship, I cannot hurt you. I will be only too glad to be of help."

The pixies ran to the little ship and chattered at the tops of their silvery voices. Yes, it would do beautifully! What luck that it happened to be there! If it hadn't, the party would have been spoilt – and the King and Queen themselves were coming!

Soon, the pixies had loaded all their food on board and settled down. One of them sat at the front and guided the ship out into the moonlit stream.

How proud the little toy ship was! Never before had it had anything but dolls aboard, and they couldn't do anything but sit still and stare at the sky. But these little fairy folk chattered and laughed. They ran here and there across its decks, they leaned over the side and tried to dip their fingers in the water. It was great fun for the little ship!

Out it went over the stream, sailing most beautifully. The wind filled its sails and it floated like a swan, proud and handsome.

The fairies on the other side cried out in delight – they were so grateful that the *Lucy Ann* had saved their party. And would you believe it, at that very moment the King and Queen of Fairyland arrived, riding in their golden carriage!

They watched the little boat too, and how pleased they were to see it come safely to the bank. All the fairies cheered, and the ship's blue sail trembled with joy.

The *Lucy Ann* stayed by the bank to watch the party. It smiled to see the little folk dancing to their pixie music.

And then the King and Queen asked the little ship if it would take them for a sail up the stream in the moonlight. What an honour!

"Oh, Your Majesties, I would love to," said the ship. "But the stream is so strong that I find it difficult to sail against it."

"We will help you by a magic spell," said the King. "You shall take us far up the stream, to the place where the flowers grow, and when we are tired of sailing, our butterfly-carriage will bring us home. Ho there, pixies, bid our carriage follow us up the stream!"

The King and Queen stepped into the boat and off it went, sailing easily against the current, for the King had used his magic to help the ship.

How enjoyable it was, sailing along in the moonlight! The little ship had never felt so happy or so proud – after all, it was carrying the King and Queen of Fairyland.

It was a beautiful night. On either side, the banks were lined with trees that shone silver in the moonlight, and the little waves on the stream looked like silver, too.

Bats fluttered silently overhead and the old owl hooted to them as he flew by. All around them the little ship fancied it could hear the sound of fairy voices, singing a gentle lullaby. It was a most exciting journey.

After a lovely long sail the King spoke to the little ship once more.

"We will land now," he said. "Draw in to the bank, little ship. See where our butterfly carriage awaits us!"

The ship saw a beautiful carriage drawn by four yellow butterflies. It was waiting by a fence on the bank, overhung with beautiful roses.

The *Lucy Ann* sailed to the side and waited there while the King and Queen got out. Then, as it looked about, the little ship gave a glad cry.

"Why! This is where Mary and Timothy played with me this morning!" it said. "If only I could stay here, then they might find me in the morning!"

"Of course you shall stay here," said the King. "I will tie you to a stick."

So he tied the little ship tightly to a twig in the bank. The King then said goodbye and thanked the ship very much for all its help.

"I will turn your sail into a silver one, in reward for your kindness," said the Queen. In a trice the ship's blue sail became one of glittering silver thread. It was really splendid. Then the King and Queen mounted their butterfly carriage and off they rode in the moonlight.

Soon it was dawn. The ship slept for a little while, and then woke up. It was proud of its glittering silver sail, and it longed for Mary and Timothy to come down to the stream to see it.

The children came running down before breakfast – and how they stared when they saw the little toy ship!

"Look at that beautiful ship!" cried Mary. "Where did it come from? It's just like ours, only it has a silver sail!"

"I wonder who tied it to that stick," said Timothy, puzzled. "Nobody comes down here but us."

"Ooh, look, Timothy – it *is* our ship! It's called *Lucy Ann*!" cried Mary, in excitement. "See, its name is on the side so it *must* be ours. But how did it get its beautiful sail, and who tied it up here for us to find!"

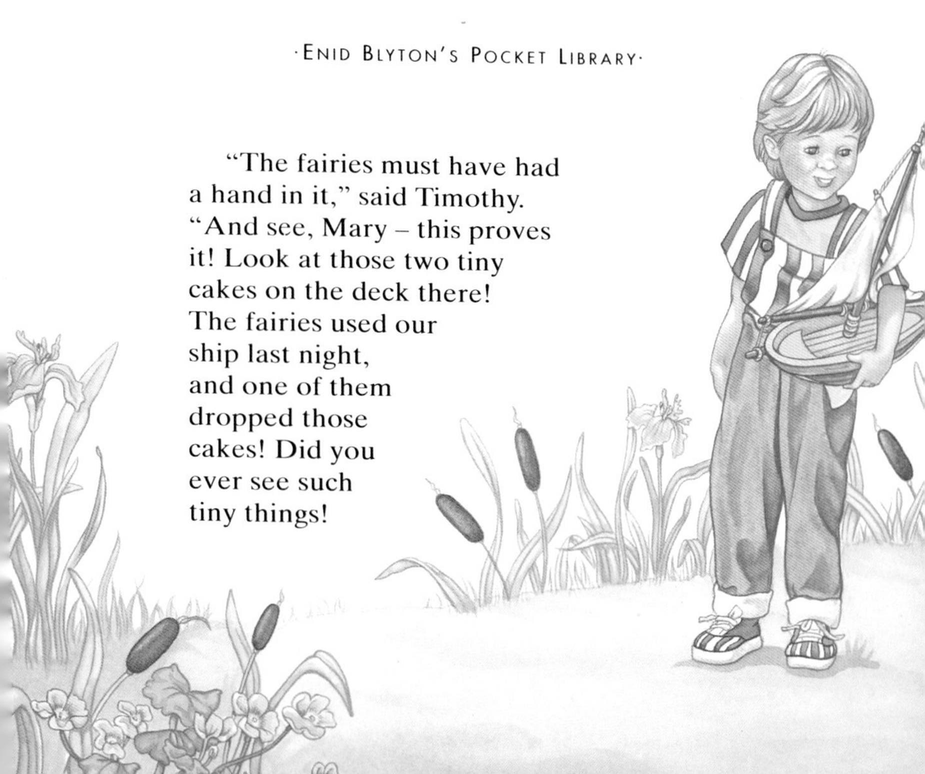

"The fairies must have had a hand in it," said Timothy. "And see, Mary – this proves it! Look at those two tiny cakes on the deck there! The fairies used our ship last night, and one of them dropped those cakes! Did you ever see such tiny things!

Shall we eat them?"

"Yes – but let's save them till tonight, then maybe we'll see the fairies too!" cried Mary.

They took their ship from the water and ran to tell Mummy all about it. She was so surprised to see its silver sail!

The ship was glad to be back in the toy cupboard. And how it enjoyed itself telling all the other toys of its adventures!

Mary and Timothy are going to eat those pixie cakes tonight. I do wonder what will happen, don't you?

Teach your child SWIMMING

B.E. Gorton

National Technical Officer to the Amateur Swimming Assoc

Teach your child SWIMMING

B.E. Gorton

LEPUS BOOKS
106, HAMPSTEAD ROAD, LONDON NW1 2LS

Photographs by W. R. Hart.

An associate company of Henry Kimpton Ltd.
106, Hampstead Road, London NW1 2LS

ISBN 0 86019 022 6 (limp)
0 86019 026 9 (case)

Computer Typesetting by
Print Origination, Orrell Mount, Hawthorne Road,
Bootle, Merseyside, L20 6NS

Printed Offset Litho in Great Britain by
Cox & Wyman Ltd, London, Fakenham and Reading

Contents

Foreword

By J.M. Noble, Chairman of the Amateur Swimming Association Education Committee.

How appropriate it is that this book should be written at a time when more and more parents are seeking sound advice as to the best ways of helping their children to become competent swimmers.

Few persons can be better qualified to give this advice than Mr. B.E. Gorton, for many years now a National Development Officer with the Amateur Swimming Association, with a vast experience of all facets of the sport. Teaching, lecturing and demonstrating up and down the country, he has done much to popularise swimming and to introduce thousands of people of all ages–from baby learners to the quite elderly–to the exciting experience of swimming for the first time. He is equally at home with top-level swimmers and complete novices and has in his time coached international and Olympic swimmers.

In this well-illustrated and easy-to-follow book, Mr Gorton has drawn on his wide experience to provide parents with the basic knowledge which will enable them to teach their children to swim, starting from the first visits up to the development of higher water skills. It says much for his skill that he does so in a manner simple enough to satisfy the needs of those with little or no previous knowledge, yet still provides valuable advice and suggestions for the more knowledgeable parent who wants to help his child improve his general level of swimming.

All the main swimming strokes are fully dealt with and the appropriate teaching stages carefully described. So too are the teaching of the starts and turns for each stroke, together with such other water skills as survival swimming, underwater swimming and diving. Of special interest to parents and children alike will be the various incentive awards of the Amateur Swimming Association which have been listed.

I warmly commend this book to all parents interested in teaching their children to swim or to help them become better swimmers.

Part 1
The Correct Start

Introduction
Teaching the Baby Stage
Teaching the Slightly Older Child
The Best Stroke
Teaching the Next Stage

Introduction

The purpose of this book initially, is to explain in a straightforward way how to teach your child to swim, and secondly how to improve his ability.

Swimming can be fun and immensely satisfying, and provides a lifetime of enjoyable activity. Although water can be enjoyed, it can also be dangerous, especially for a child who cannot swim. It is essential, for safety reasons alone, that a young person should learn to swim as soon as possible.

A mother or father is the natural person to teach a young child, and provided that there is sufficient knowledge and understanding, a parent will continue to gain satisfaction as the child grows older.

TEACHING THE BABY STAGE

The best time to start teaching your child to swim is during his first bath time. Provided that your baby is introduced sensibly he will have no fear of water.

It is important at this early stage that you should *never leave your baby unattended in his bath.*

Before you bath your child, make sure that he is not hungry or tired, as both of these conditions will make him fractious and cause him to cry—this can be interpreted by some parents as fear.

In the early stages, use a small baby bath, and only use soap and shampoo made specially for babies. Never rush this bath and always allow plenty of time for a play session.

As soon as possible, allow your baby to lie on his back in the water while you support his head. Occasionally splash water onto his face, using only a trickle in the early stages. He will soon become accustomed to having more water splashed over him. This is very important and should be a feature of every bath time.

Baby will soon be able to be transferred into a large bath. Fill the bath to a depth of three inches. Encourage him to kick and splash whilst still supporting his head and help him to move backwards and forwards in the water. Make a regular game of splashing water over his face and he will soon become accustomed to it.

If satisfactory progress has been made, by the time he is six months old, your baby can be introduced to a much larger pool. During the summer months and in suitably warm weather, a garden paddling pool can be used. Usually, however, it will be necessary to visit a swimming pool, preferably a shallow learners pool.

Ensure that conditions are satisfactory before you take your baby along. The water should be warm, the building should be relatively quiet and not overcrowded. The air temperature should be comfortable.

Many pools operate a 'Mums and Tots' session when other parents will bring their children along. This should prove ideal.

On your first visits allow your baby to spend a lot of time in an upright position as you support him under his arms, and making sure that he is relatively low in the water. You will now find that he will make movements resembling walking and running.

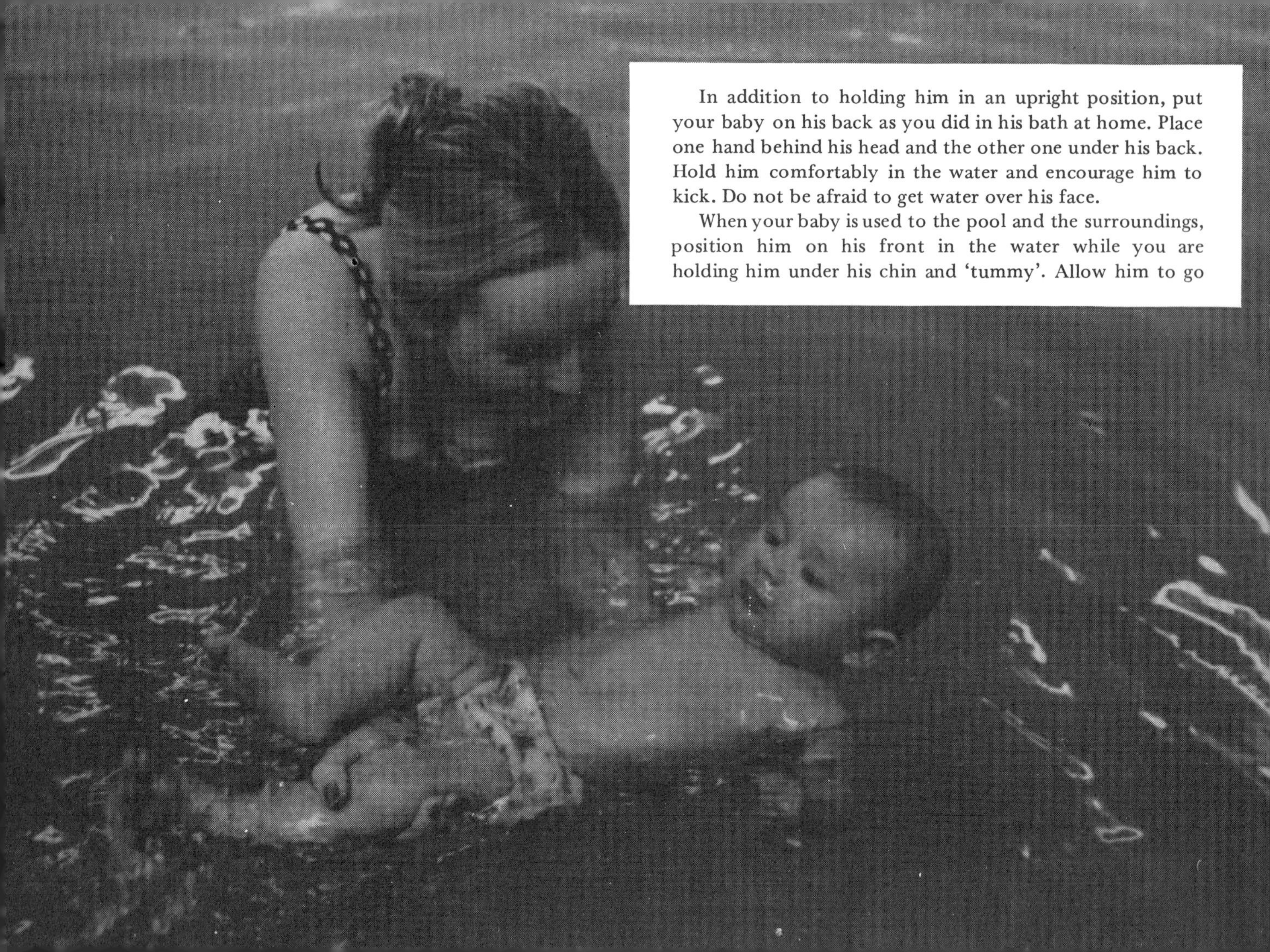

In addition to holding him in an upright position, put your baby on his back as you did in his bath at home. Place one hand behind his head and the other one under his back. Hold him comfortably in the water and encourage him to kick. Do not be afraid to get water over his face.

When your baby is used to the pool and the surroundings, position him on his front in the water while you are holding him under his chin and 'tummy'. Allow him to go

under the water momentarily. Do not, however, make too much fuss about this.

Visit the pool as often as you can and on each visit increase the amount of time he spends under the water to a maximum of five seconds at a time. Eventually allow him to do this unsupported—he may sink a little but do not panic! No harm will be done when he goes underneath the water as he will automatically hold his breath.

At this early stage only allow him to submerge once at each visit.

Summary of initial stages

1. Always be confident when handling baby.
2. Wet your baby's face and head on every opportunity.
3. Do not fuss.
4. Persevere even if your baby cries. On the other hand do not allow him to become distressed.
5. Encourage plenty of movement, especially kicking.
6. Allow front and back floating unaided for a short period on each visit.
7. Progress gradually.

DEVELOPMENT WITH THE VERY YOUNG CHILD

Your child has now reached the stage when he can proceed unaided, although he will wear some form of buoyancy aid. You will, of course, be close by and constantly reassuring him with your presence.

There are a large number of buoyancy aids which you can buy. Some of these are inexpensive and others are more sophisticated. The simplest and most effective aids for your child at this age are arm bands. Very young children are usually top heavy and arm bands prevent the wearer from rolling into a lying position with his head and face in the water. Arm bands are usually sold in different sizes, so be sure to buy one which fits firmly.

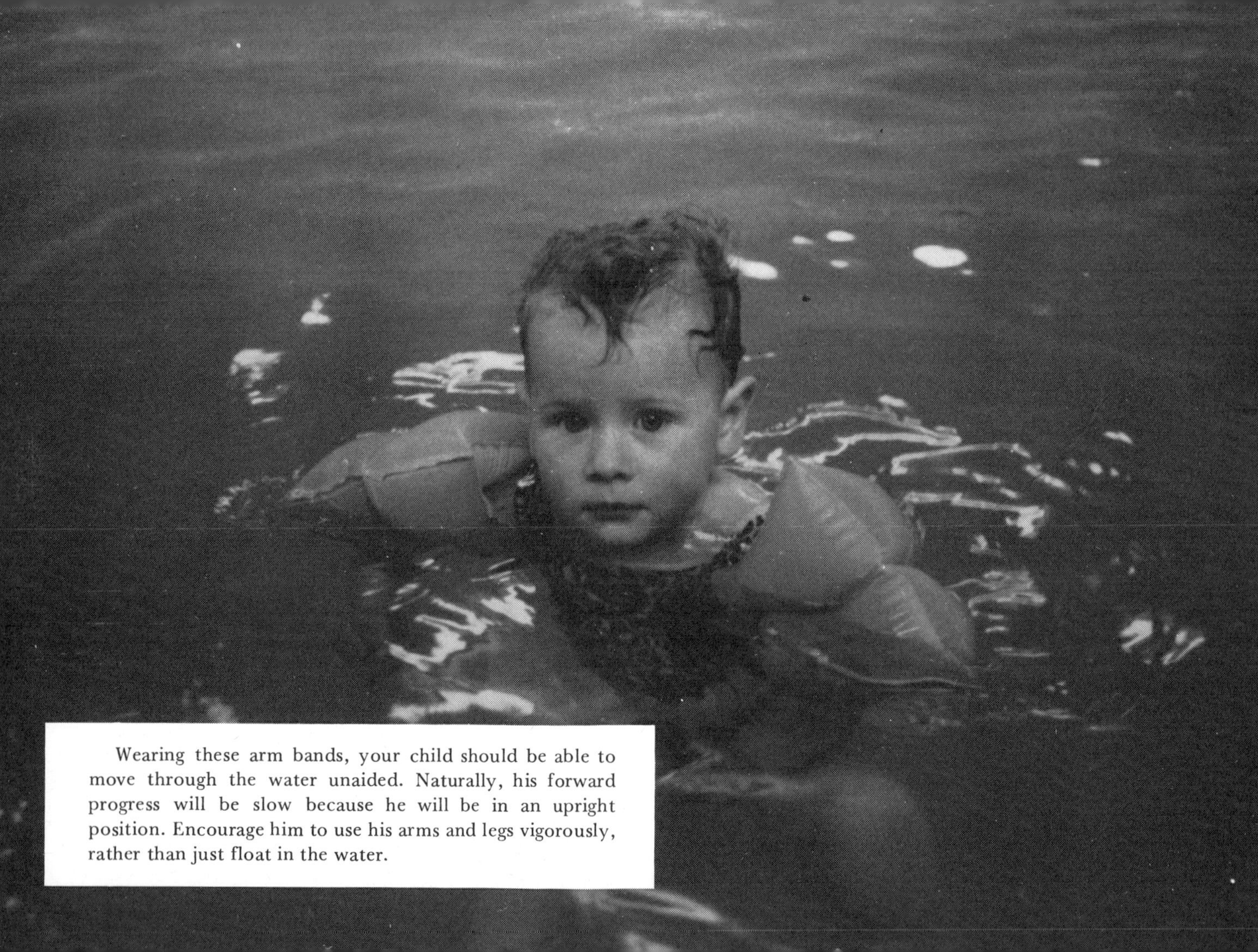

Wearing these arm bands, your child should be able to move through the water unaided. Naturally, his forward progress will be slow because he will be in an upright position. Encourage him to use his arms and legs vigorously, rather than just float in the water.

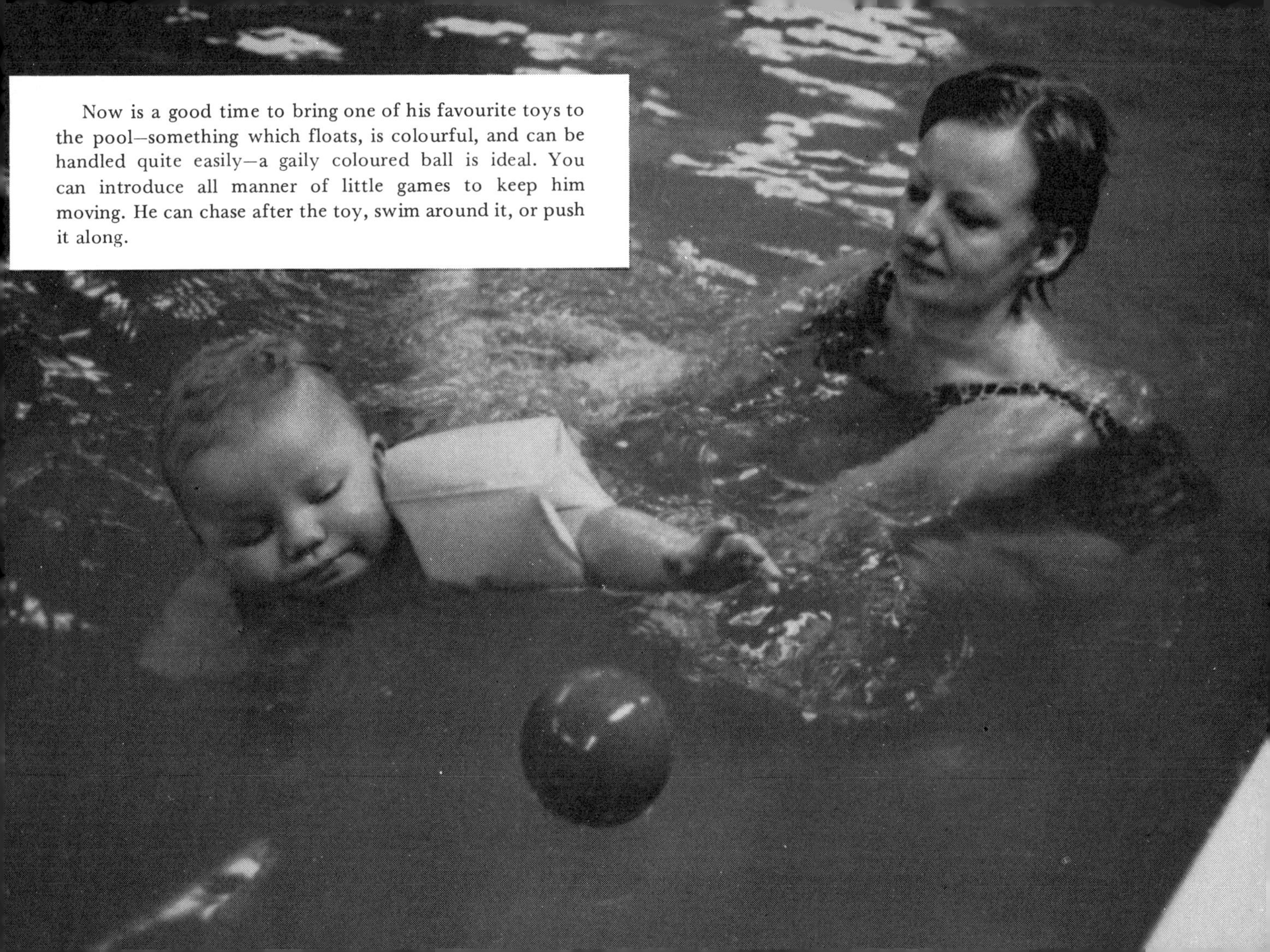

Now is a good time to bring one of his favourite toys to the pool—something which floats, is colourful, and can be handled quite easily—a gaily coloured ball is ideal. You can introduce all manner of little games to keep him moving. He can chase after the toy, swim around it, or push it along.

Occasionally help him by directing his arms and legs manually. Initially, he can use a simple dog paddle or he can move his hands in small circles.

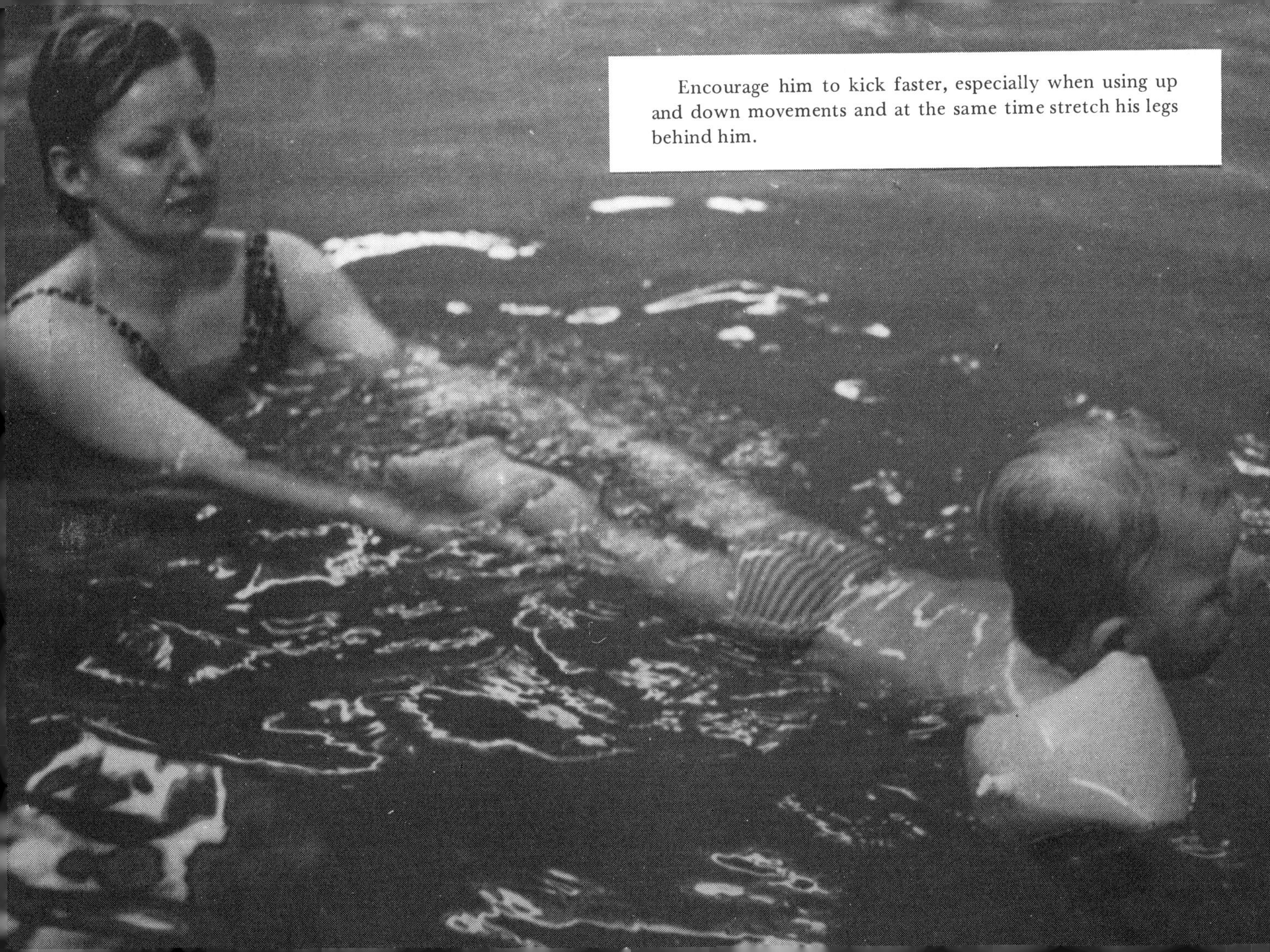

Encourage him to kick faster, especially when using up and down movements and at the same time stretch his legs behind him.

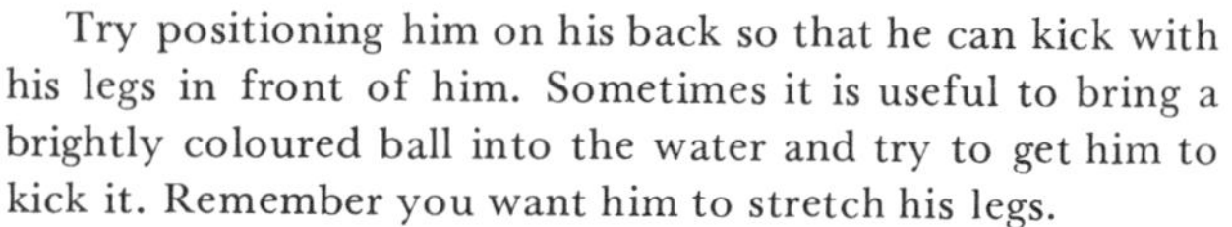

Try positioning him on his back so that he can kick with his legs in front of him. Sometimes it is useful to bring a brightly coloured ball into the water and try to get him to kick it. Remember you want him to stretch his legs.

Do not expect too much from him at this stage, because all you are attempting to do is play with him and make him use his arms and legs.

You should spend part of each visit practising the activities which you started from the beginning, when you were not using buoyancy aids.

Continue to accustom him to accepting his face in the water. Tow him slowly around the pool with his face submerged for short periods. Hold him with one hand under his chest and the other hand under his chin. If he does not mind his face in the water, you can now begin to expect him to have his face submerged at frequent short intervals. You should use your hand which is holding him under his chin to raise and lower his head as you are towing him around the pool.

Occasionally allow him to float unaided both on his front and on his back.

As your child becomes more confident and when he is able to stand and begin simple jumps, he can jump into your arms from the pool side. He will soon progress to jumping in when you will allow him to go under the water.

If you have followed this guidance, there is no reason why, by the age of two, your child should not be able to move through the water unaided for short periods of time.

You will of course, need to maintain regular attendance throughout the year, otherwise you may find that you will have to start all over again.

Do not expect that your child will be able to copy the swimming strokes of older children. The aims at this stage are confidence building, helping your child to be safe in water, and able to move short distances unaided.

Give him plenty of practice at what he appears to do well, and ensure that he concludes each visit to the pool on a successful note.

Summary

1. Introduce arm bands.
2. Encourage pulling and kicking, assist him if necessary.
3. Continue to encourage him to put his face in the water.
4. Progress to jumping into the water.
5. Use plenty of praise.
6. Allow plenty of time to practice at what he does well.

TEACHING THE SLIGHTLY OLDER CHILD

Much of the information which has already been given also applies to an older child who is learning to swim.

It is essential to realise that before you can teach your child to swim properly, you must aim to build his confidence.

Unfortunately, some older children are frightened of water, because they have not been given the opportunity of getting used to it in a swimming environment. Parents should take their child to a swimming pool as early as possible.

Before you take him for the first time, go to the pool yourself so that you can familiarise yourself with the building and the general procedure. You can then decide when is the best time to take him and give him some confidence by explaining what to expect when he gets there. If he is apprehensive about going, take him along just to show him how other children are enjoying themselves.

Before the first session, spend as much time as possible at home getting him used to having water splashed over his face and head—a shower is very useful for doing this. Encourage him to put his face fully in his bath, but only when you are close by.

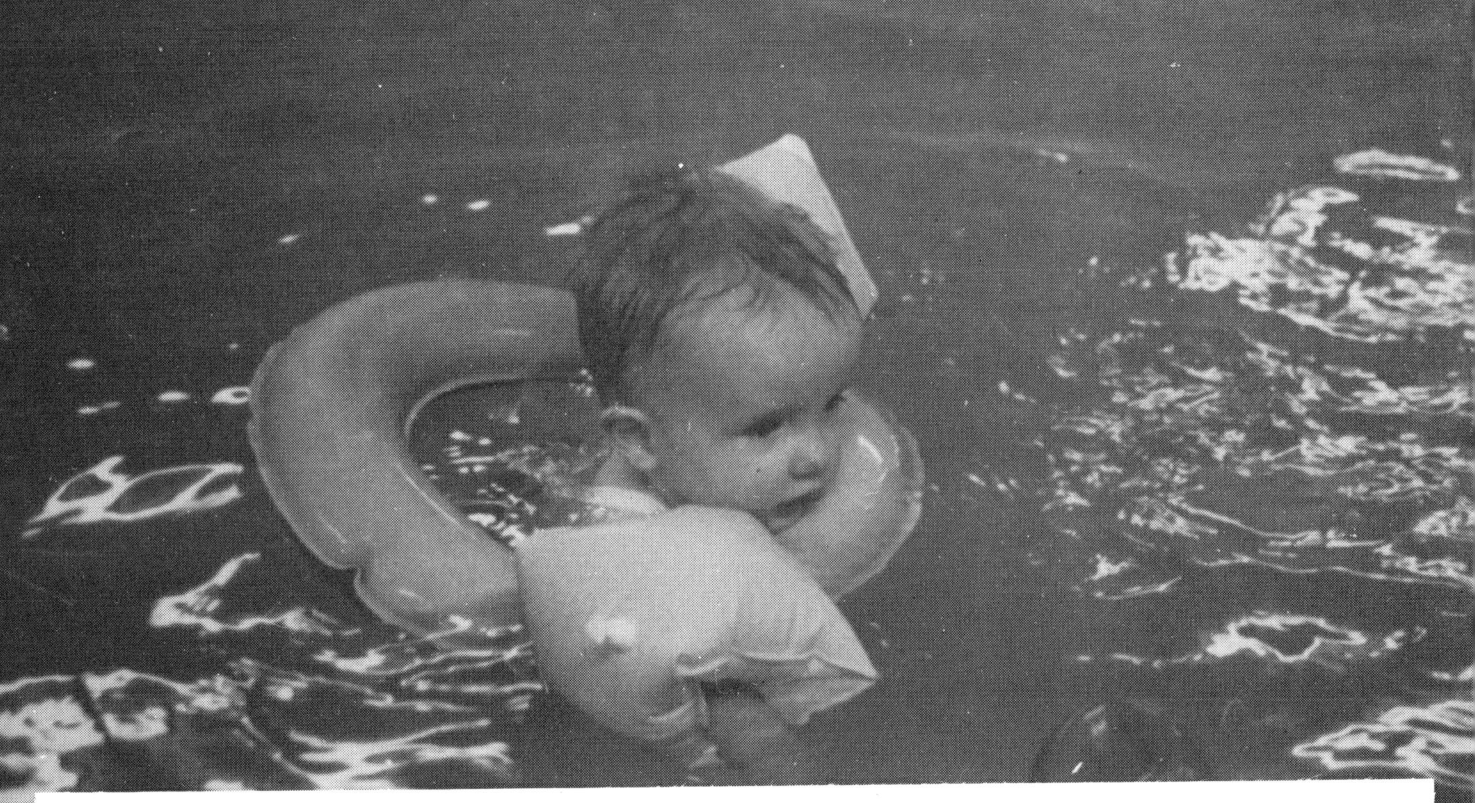

Continue to concentrate on these activities until he has enough confidence to accept them happily in a swimming pool.

Do not rush the initial visit—let him sit on the pool-side and splash his feet, and when he is ready let him enter the water using the steps. Ideally he should be able to stand comfortably in the water. Unfortunately some pools are a little too deep for very young children, so therefore be sure you use adequate buoyancy aids. Using a combination of rings and armbands will be found helpful if your child is nervous. Less nervous children will accept either quite happily.

As you will be in the water and close to your child, either aid is safe, but arm bands are preferable for very young children. Rings are suitable for bigger and stronger children for they allow them to adopt a flatter body position in the water.

Even when using buoyancy aids, your child might be unsure of himself and will not take his feet off the bottom of the pool. If this is the case, let him build his confidence by walking about the pool. Suggest that he changes direction and experiences walking sideways and backwards as well as forwards. Most children feel safer when they slide their feet along the bottom rather than picking them up as they would on land.

Eventually when he is more at ease, ask him to place both of his forearms along your forearms and get him to float in a sitting position. Gradually lessen the support you are giving, until he is able to sit unaided by you. Now it is a simple matter to get him to use his arms in some form of pulling movement. Ask him to kick at the same time. How he uses his limbs at this stage does not matter. You will suggest that he stretches out and pulls himself copying a dog paddle or with both arms at the same time.

As his confidence grows, he will begin to move faster in the water. Encourage him to use bigger, slower and more powerful movements, especially with his arms.

At this stage, if he is using both sets of buoyancy aids, persuade him to discard one of them.

Suggest to him that he tries different ways of moving his arms and legs, as well as using different body positions and moving in different directions.

Suggestions to copy:

Pull with alternate arms.
Pull with both arms.
Change position from your front to your back.
Swim on your back.
Swim sideways.
Swim in large circles.
Swim zig zag.
Swim using your legs on their own.
Swim bringing arms out of the water.
Swim using only one arm.

Confidence-building activities can be made more exciting by introducing a ball into the water (check first that the pool authorities will allow you to do this).

Suggestions to follow:

Swim after the ball (use direction and positions).
Swim and push it along in front of you (use alternate arms and then both arms).
Swim and use different parts of the body with which to push it.
Sit in the water and kick the ball (a good practice for swimming on the back).
Swim around the ball.

Combinations of activities are limitless. They are aimed at making your child as familiar with the water as possible.

The age of your child will affect the extent to which he understands your instructions. A young child will copy you, so be prepared to show him what to do. Remember you are not trying to teach proper swimming strokes at this stage, but you are aiming for confidence and progression through the water.

Do not neglect to get him to put his face and head under water. Suggest that he pushes a ball through the water with his chin at first, then with his nose and finally with the top of his head. He can try this walking, but as soon as possible it should be attempted in a swimming position.

Now he is ready to swim for short distances with his face in the water, and he can discard his buoyancy aid. If the confidence activities have been well done, he will be able to swim unaided for short distances. These distances will soon lengthen as he learns how to swim and get his breath at the same time.

He can achieve the same success whilst swimming on his back. Help him to lie flat on his back with his eyes looking vertically up to the ceiling and his 'tummy' high in the water. Some children can kick quite effectively with an alternate leg action in this position, while they move their hands, in an outwards and inwards direction with palms facing the bottom of the pool. (This is called sculling–see pages 86 & 87 Figs. 118 a, b, c.)

If your child can get into this position easily and unaided and progresses through the water, he is ready to try it without his buoyancy aid.

Some children are more nervous than others and do not like to have their buoyancy aids taken from them too soon. In such cases confidence can be maintained if air is gradually let out of their buoyancy aids until eventually there is none left.

'Frogmens' flippers can be useful to the learner. Unfortunately, they are not sold in very small sizes, but if you can get a pair to fit your child, he will be able to move quite fast through the water when using a normal up and down movement of his feet and legs. This speed will give him confidence and he will soon be able to swim using only one flipper which in turn should be discarded.

WHICH IS THE BEST STROKE WITH WHICH TO START SWIMMING?

It is important to let your child try different swimming strokes when he is learning. When he is trying a breast stroke movement and copies it well, observe his feet. If he kicks naturally with flat feet, he will probably develop with this stroke.

If he easily acquires a good position on his back and moves well, he will probably prefer this style.

Most children find a combination of dog paddle and front crawl leg kicking most comfortable. A few develop breast stroke circling of the arms with front crawl kicking. Older children perform well by bringing their arms out of the water with an alternating action similar to normal front crawl.

The most important factor at this stage is to allow natural movements which give confidence and produce forward movement.

Summary

1. Plan your first visit to the pool.
2. Start immediately with adequate buoyancy aids.
3. Emphasise plenty of movements of arms and legs.
4. As soon as possible get your child's face in the water.
5. Practise all strokes.
6. Reduce buoyancy aids as progress develops.

TEACHING THE NEXT STAGE

When your child is able to swim unaided he should persevere with the following essential practices which will form the basis of his future success.

1. First of all he must develop stamina, which will be gained from swimming longer distances. At this stage, he will only be able to complete half a dozen strokes which will enable him to swim four or five metres. Do not worry about his style, it will improve as he develops the ability to increase the distance he can swim. You will want him to attempt different strokes, but only demand greater distances when he is using his favourite stroke. At this stage he will probably be rushing his movements, so suggest he swims in slow motion. He will not be able to do this properly, but if he tries, it will help to slow the stroke down. Suggest that he stretches in the water or that he makes himself as long as possible as he is swimming. Always encourage him to make large movements especially with his arms when he is at this stage.
2. He must practise a lot of kicking as this will improve his poise and balance in the water as well as aiding propulsion. However, do not let him practise breast stroke leg kicking unless he has the ability to kick backwards with flat feet. (see page 33).
   In the first place he may have to practise leg kicking whilst he holds onto the sides of the pool, but as soon as possible get him to use a kicking board. Try to get a large kicking board for him to use (a small one does not give enough support). If these are not available, try using two small ones held one under each arm. When he is kicking, get him to hold the board at arms length with his hands holding it on either side and

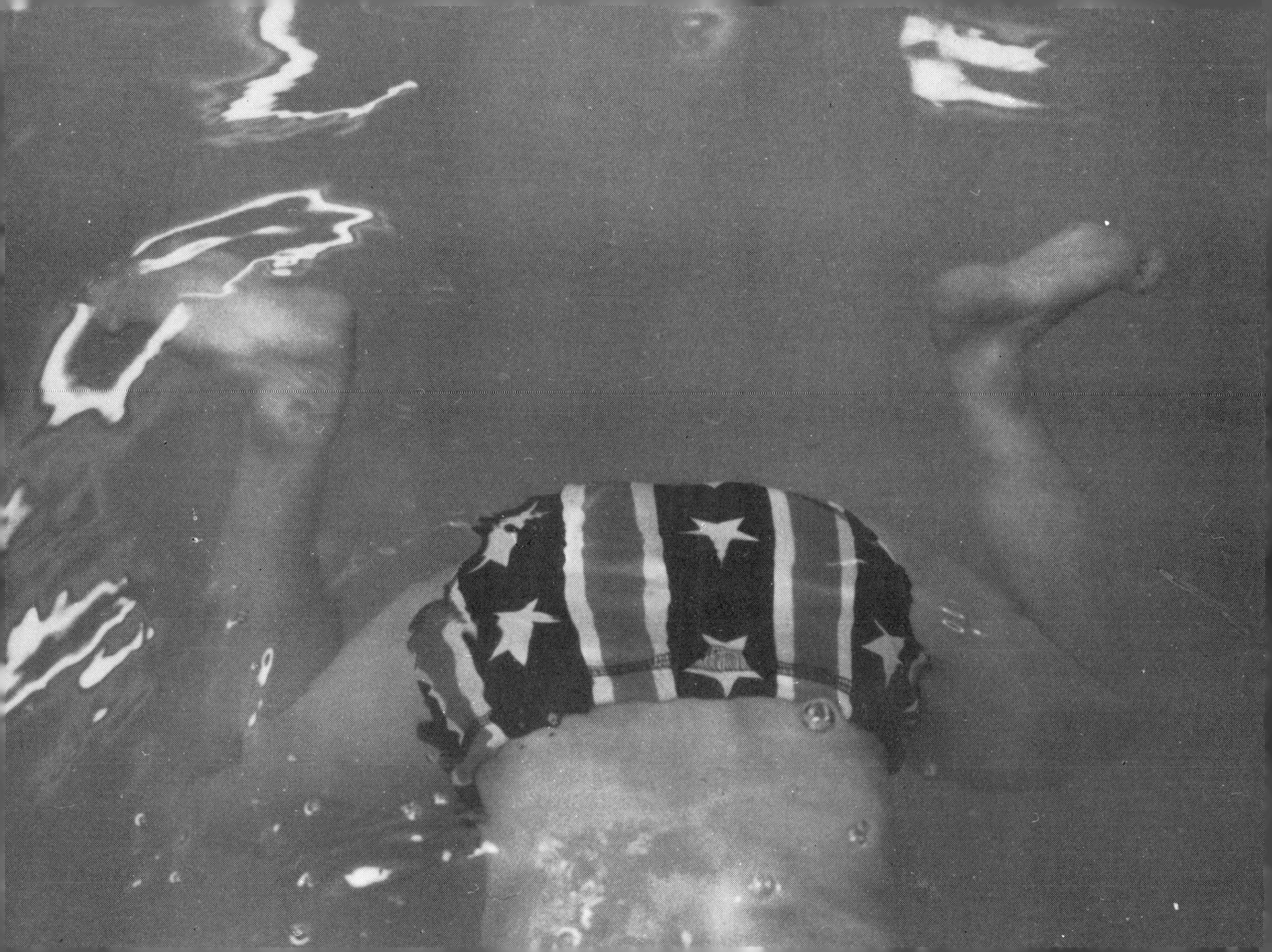

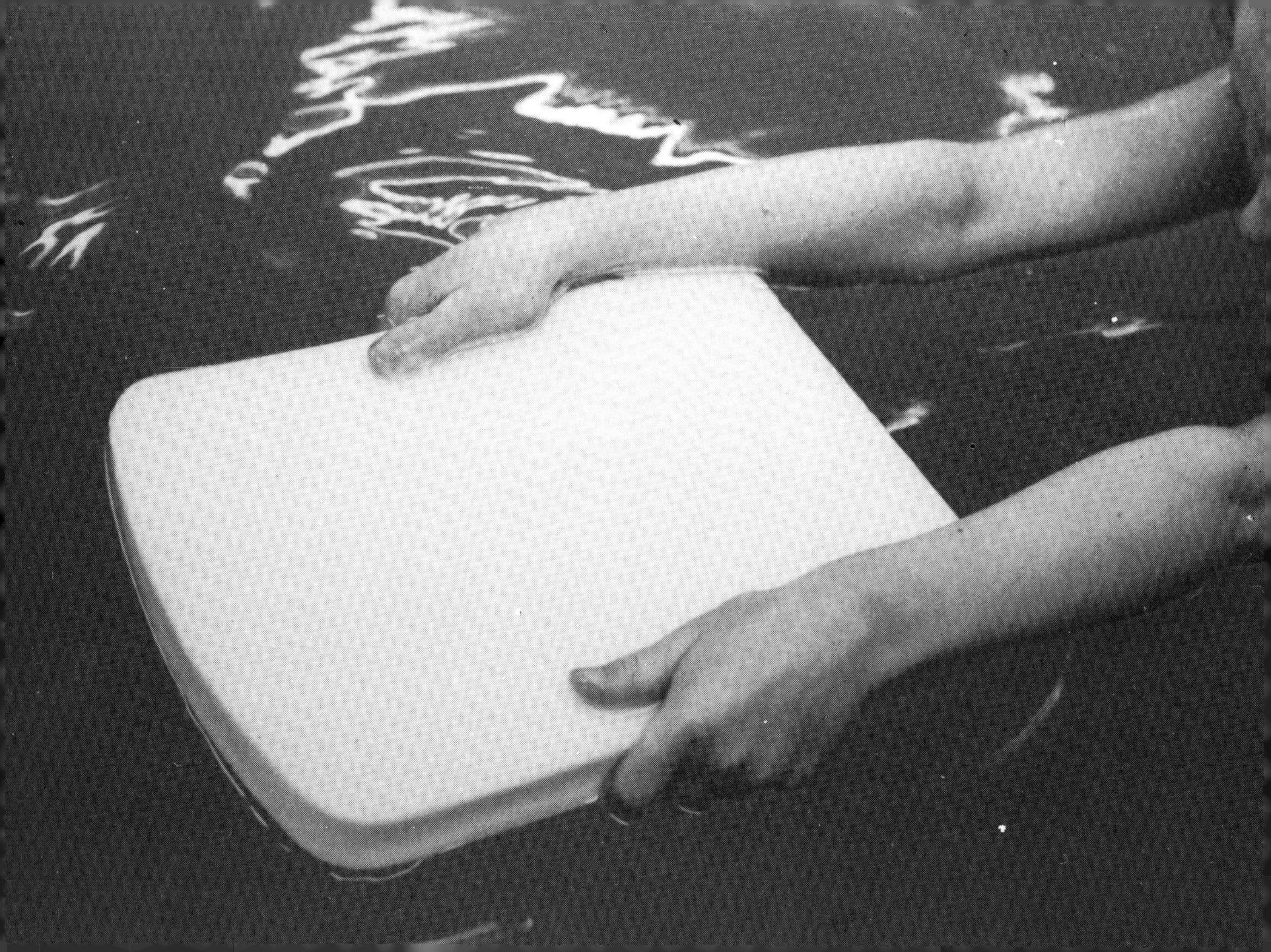

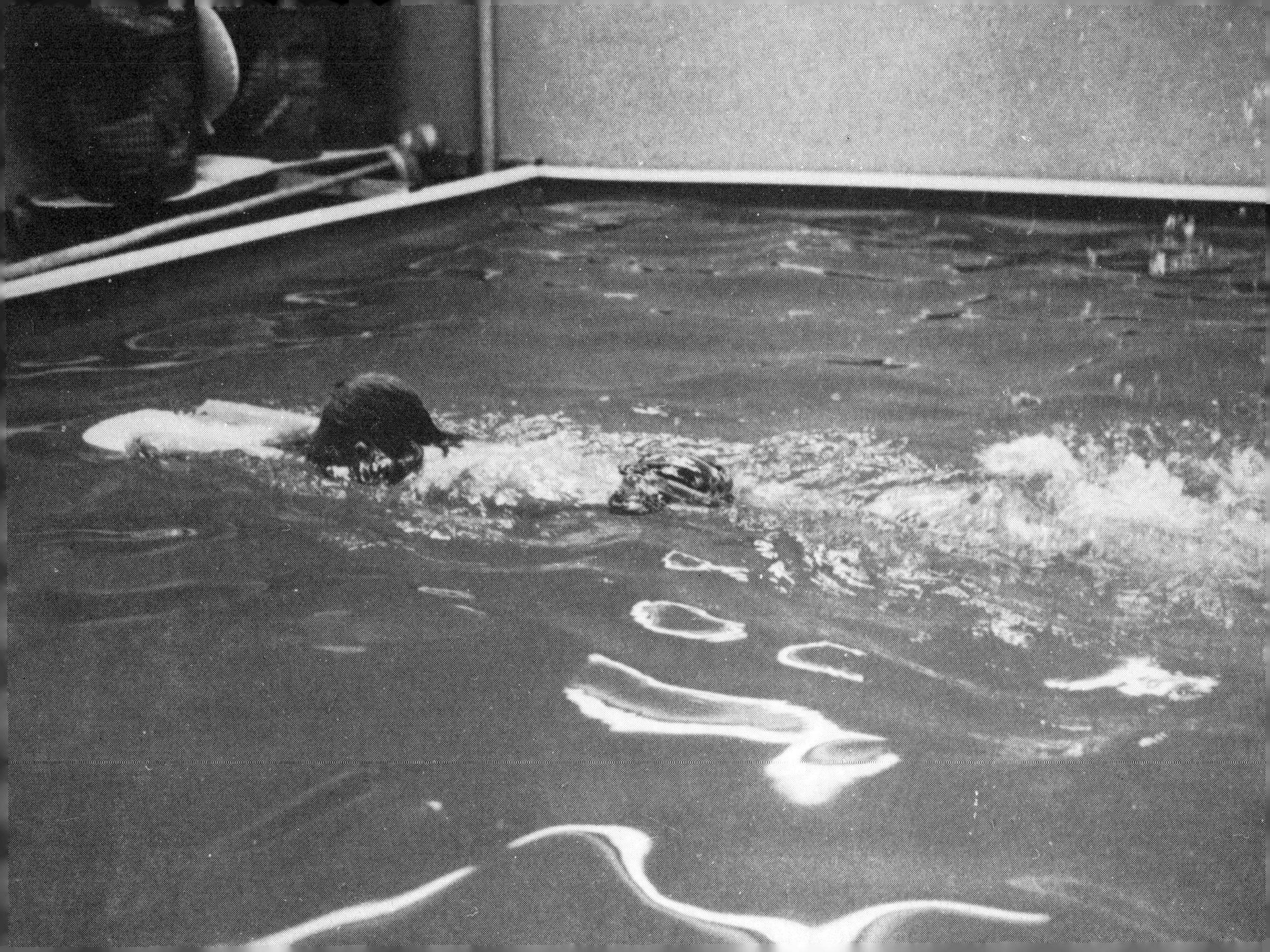

halfway along its length (see page 34). An explanation of how to perform the correct leg kick is included in each stroke section.

3. He should persevere in swimming for part of the time with his face submerged and at the same time learning how to exhale into the water (see page 35). A competent swimmer breathes out into the water and breathes in as soon as his mouth breaks the surface (this does not apply to the back stroke). When he can do this properly, not only will he learn to relax as he swims, but he will flatten out and become more streamlined. At first he can learn to breathe out whilst he is standing with his face submerged. (Fig. 1) The important thing to emphasise is that he has to blow the air out forcibly. Get him to imagine that he is trying to blow up a balloon in one forceful blow. When he has acquired the ability to do this he should then learn to breathe in and out repeatedly until it becomes natural to him.
In this respect it will help him to practise bobbing up and down out of the water. He can develop his breathing as he holds a float and practises a front crawl flutter kick. (Fig. 2)

Fig. 1

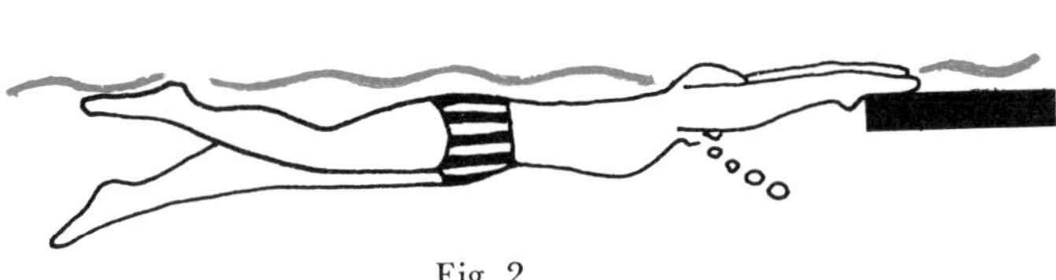

Fig. 2

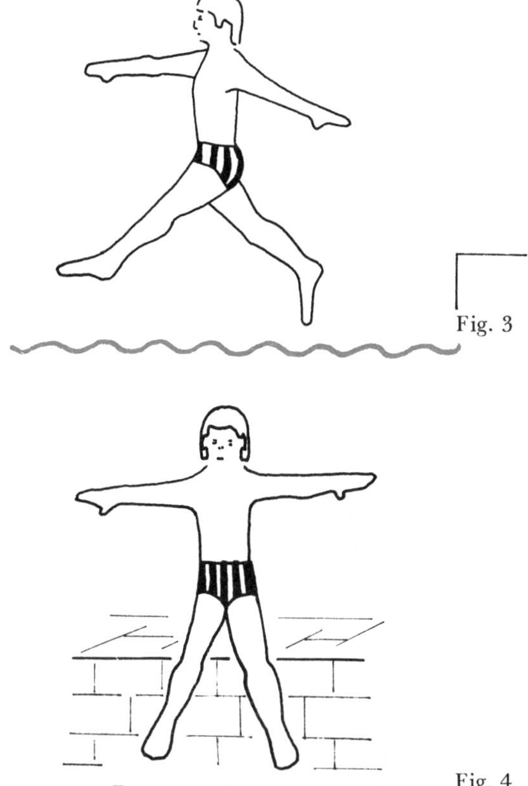

Fig. 3

Fig. 4

4. It will be useful for him to develop simple skills which will increase his confidence and ability.

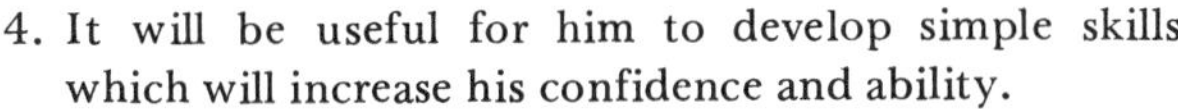

Some of them are as follows:

Jumping into the water from the side. (Fig. 3)
Jumping and making shapes in the air. (Fig. 4)
Jumping and turning different directions in the air. (Fig. 5)
Picking up objects from the bottom of the pool. (Fig. 6)
Swimming through other peoples legs.
Hand standing.
Push and gliding on and under the surface. (Fig. 7)
Somersaults in the water. (Fig. 8)

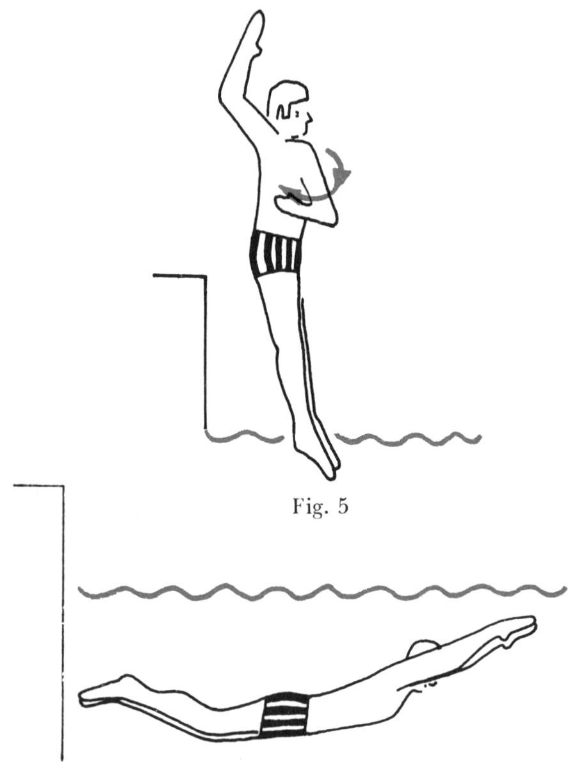

Fig. 5

Fig. 7

Fig. 6

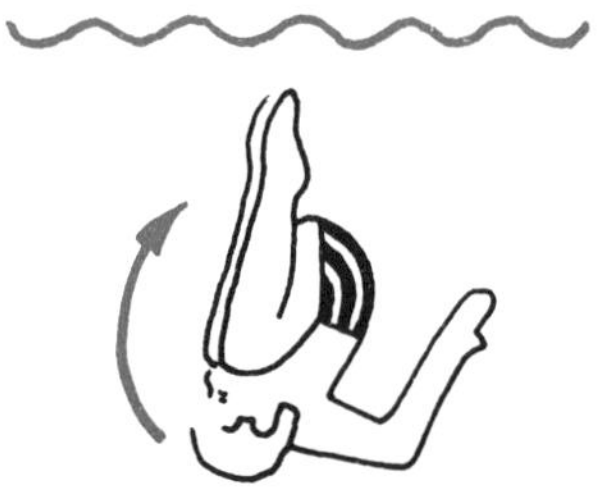

Fig. 8

Part 2
The Strokes

The Front Crawl
The Breast Stroke
The Back Stroke
The Butterfly Stroke

EARLY PRACTICES

Leg kick:

The leg kick should be performed with extended ankles. The feet should always remain in the water but should come to the surface at their highest point of the kick.

In order to help your child develop good swimming habits get him to imagine that there is a kicking board floating on the surface half an inch beyond his extended feet. Get him to kick upwards and downwards so that on the up kick the soles of his feet try to touch the underneath of the board. This should help him to extend his ankles (Fig. 9).

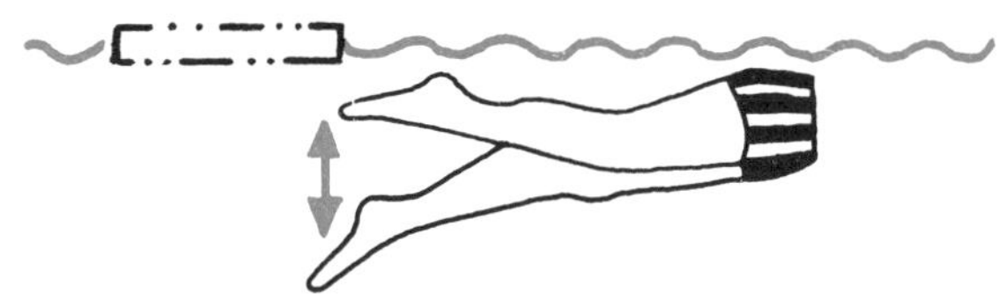

Fig. 9

Arm action

Both arms must clear the surface of the water alternately when swimming front crawl. In these early stages your child may have difficulty with getting his arms out of the water. If this is the case, ask him to use straight arms when his arms are moving over the surface (Fig. 10). As soon as he can achieve this action he should be encouraged to bend the arms so that his elbow is the highest point in the recovery movement. Some children can be very successful immediately and do not have to use straight arms.

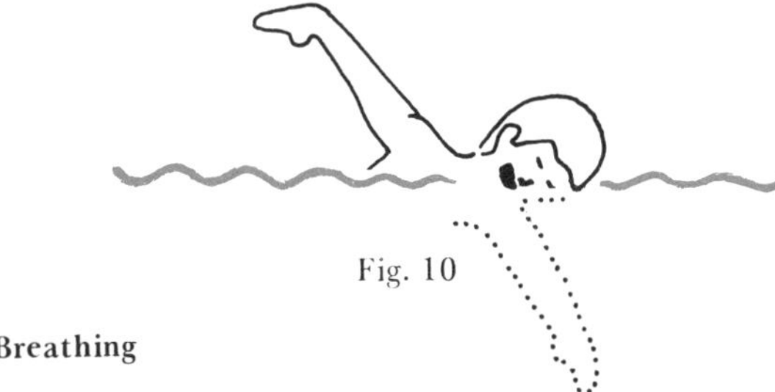

Fig. 10

Breathing

A good swimmer will always swim front crawl with his face in the water except when he breathes. To breathe in he should turn his head sideways and return it into the water to breathe out. The correct moment to inhale will be when one arm has just entered the water and the other one is just leaving the water. (Fig. 11)

If your child experiences difficulty in fitting in the breathing pattern it may be that he has not learned to blow out air into the water. This is one skill which cannot be omitted or allowed to be done badly.

If he has difficulty with this, let him practise his arm movements and breathing in a standing position. He can follow this by walking across the pool as he practises.

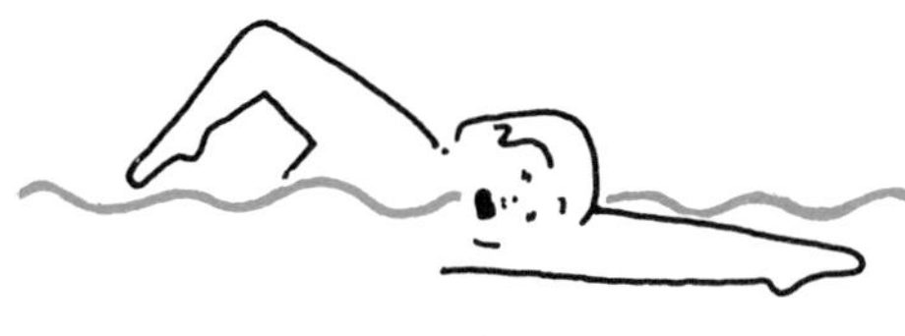

Fig. 11

DEVELOPMENT OF FRONT CRAWL

Most children obtain great benefit and satisfaction when they practise front crawl by using the following method.

Get your child to imagine that there are two kicking boards floating in the water. One is at arms length in front–submerged approximately six inches below the surface–the other board is behind the swimmer. (Fig. 12)

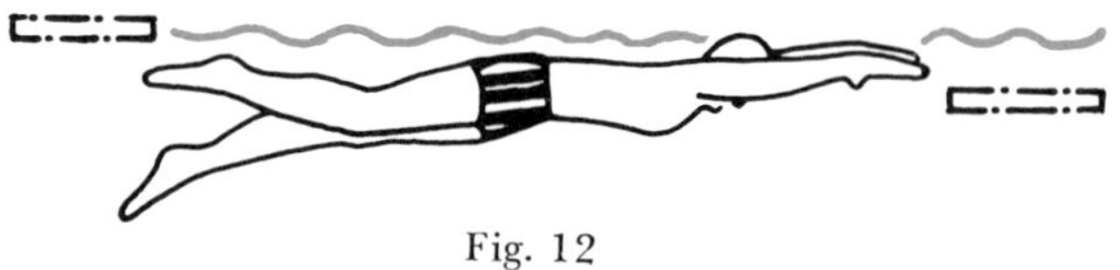

Fig. 12

To Improve Body Position

Instruct your child to look at the imaginary board which is in front as he swims the full stroke. (Fig. 13) If this is done correctly, his eyes will be open, he will be holding his head sufficiently high in the water, yet his face will be submerged and he will obtain a good position.

When he turns his head sideways in order to inhale, he should restrict his head movement to the point where he can just see the board with his lower eye. (Fig. 14)

Legs:

The kicking action and the use of the second imaginary board is explained and illustrated on page 41, Fig. 9.

Arms:

When he is recovering his arms out of the water, and when his hand has passed by his head, he should point his hand, wrist and forearm at the centre of the forward board. (Fig. 15 and photos pages 45-46).

Following on from this, his hand wrist and forearm enter the water and stretch smoothly forward and downwards to touch the nearest edge of the board (Fig. 16).

At this point, get him to imagine that he now has to pull the board backwards under the centre of the body.(Fig.17).

This action continues with a pushing movement until the board reaches a point alongside his thigh. Throughout the pulling and pushing action, the board should be turned so that it points to the floor of the pool. (Fig. 17).

Finally, the movement is completed when he imagines that he is pushing this board under the board which is following at his feet (Fig. 17).

Figs. 18a & b show the position of the arms half way through the pulling action (notice bent elbow).

Fig. 13

Fig. 14

Fig. 15

Fig. 16

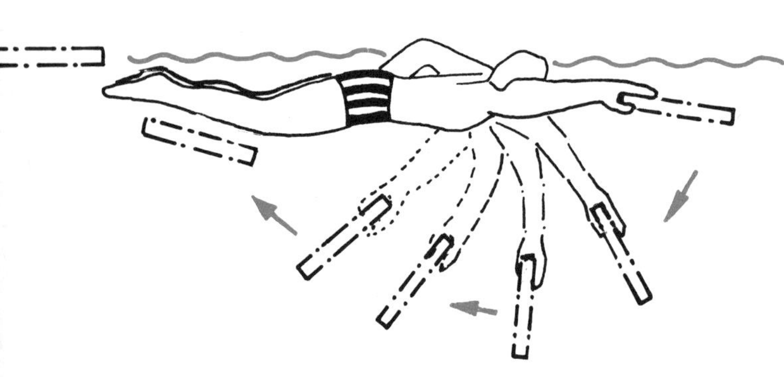

Fig. 17

Fig. 18a

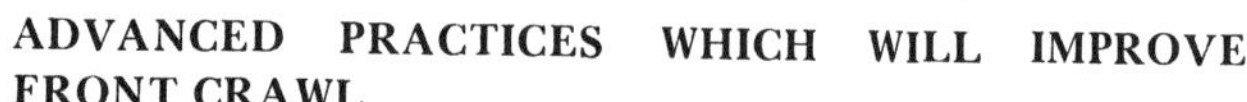

ADVANCED PRACTICES WHICH WILL IMPROVE FRONT CRAWL

Leg practices:

Flutter kick–arms extended in front without holding a kicking board. (Fig. 19)
Flutter kick–arms by the side. (Fig. 20)
Flutter kick–body on the side (Fig. 21).
Flutter kick–using kickboard–one arm forward–one arm by side with a roll for breathing. (Fig. 22)

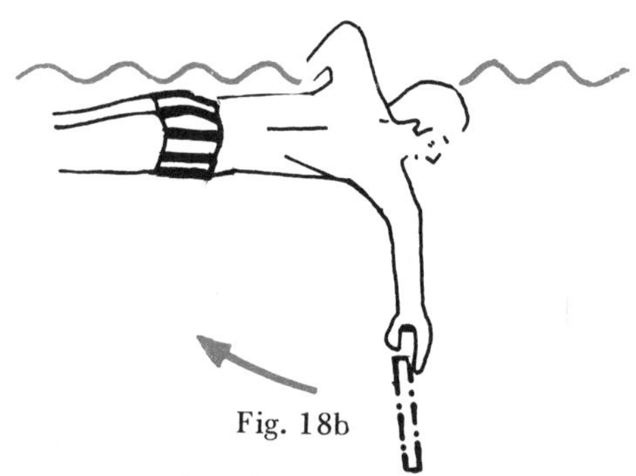

Fig. 18b

Fig. 19

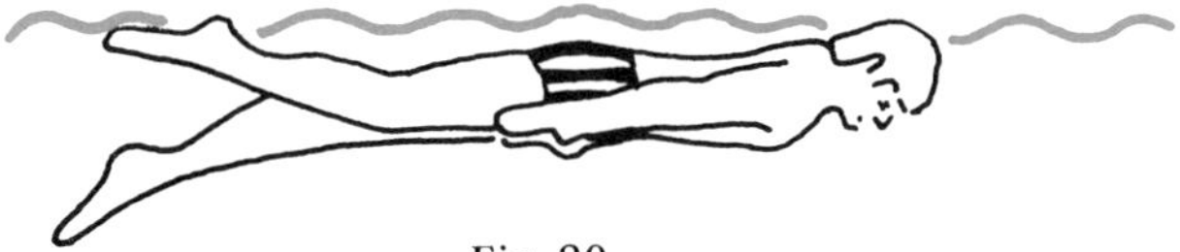

Fig. 20

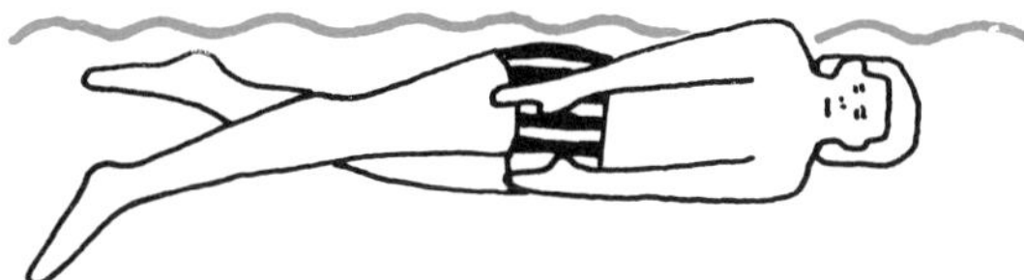

Fig. 21.

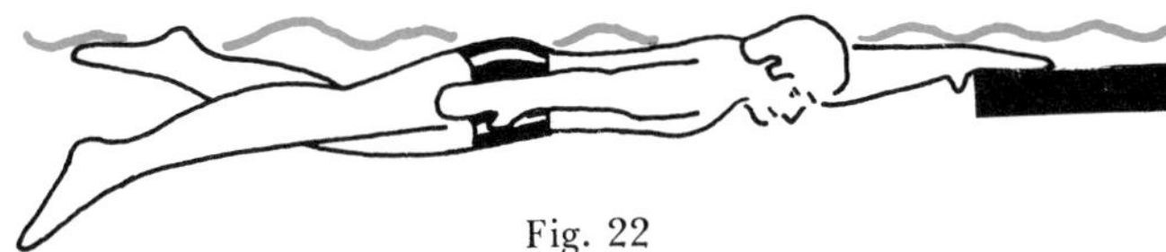

Fig. 22

Arm practices:

Arm only swimming–float held between legs at the thigh. (Fig. 23)
Arm only–rubber band around legs. (Fig. 24)
Single arm pulls–other arm extended in front. (Fig. 25)
Hand paddles used in conjunction with arm practices, will encourage correct movement and will strengthen wrist and arms. (Fig. 26)

Fig. 23

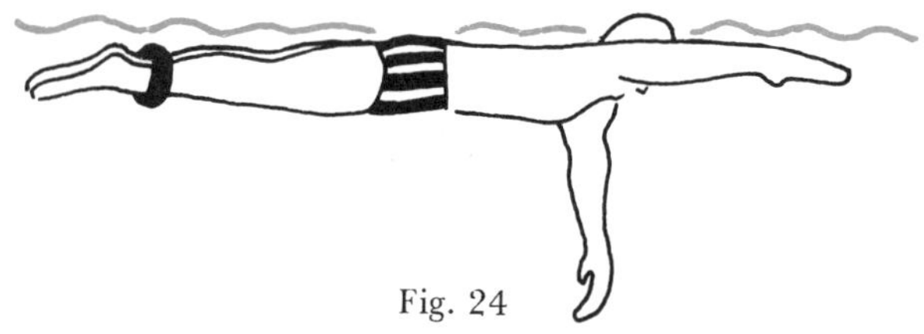
Fig. 24

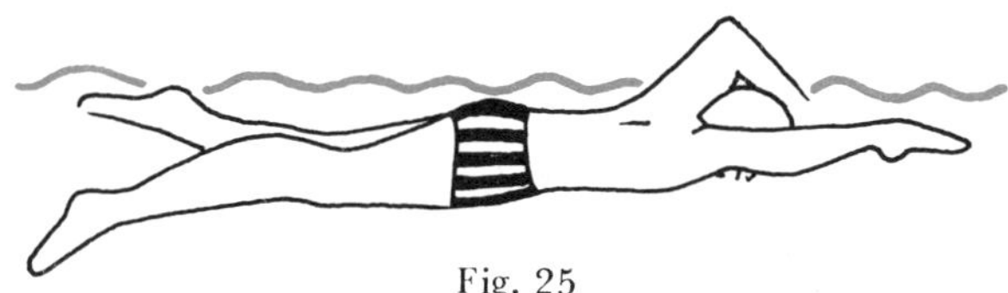
Fig. 25

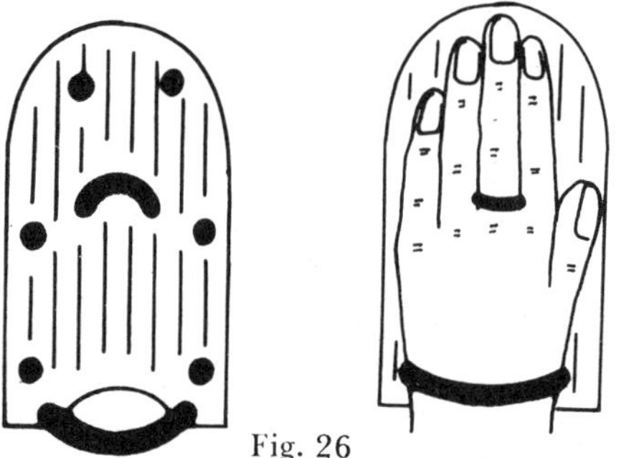
Fig. 26

BREAST STROKE

Breast stroke is simply a simultaneous pulling movement of both arms followed by a simultaneous pushing action of both legs. One action following the other continuously and smoothly.

Early learning–arms:

In the early stages, it will suffice to ask your child to pull with his hands in small circles in an outwards and backwards direction. Most beginners pull too far backwards, so be sure to get him to complete the circle in front of his shoulder.

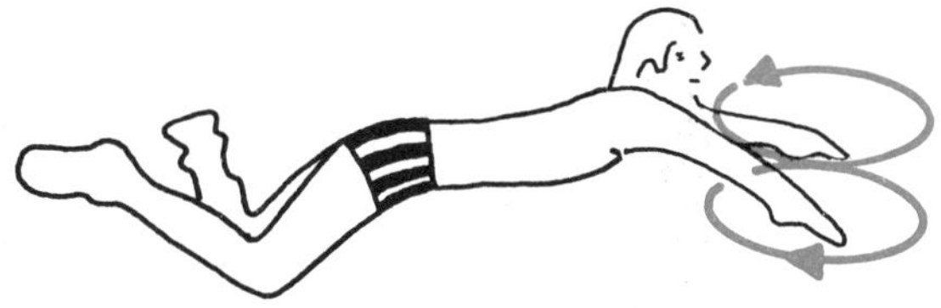
Fig. 27

As he develops confidence and proficiency grows, get him to slow the movement down.

Body position:

When he is learning the stroke, he will be most comfortable swimming with his face out of the water (Fig. 28). If he persists in swimming this way, then concentrate on the breathing exercises until he can accept a lower position of his head (Fig. 29). He does not need to have his nose and mouth out of the water unless he is inhaling (Fig. 30).

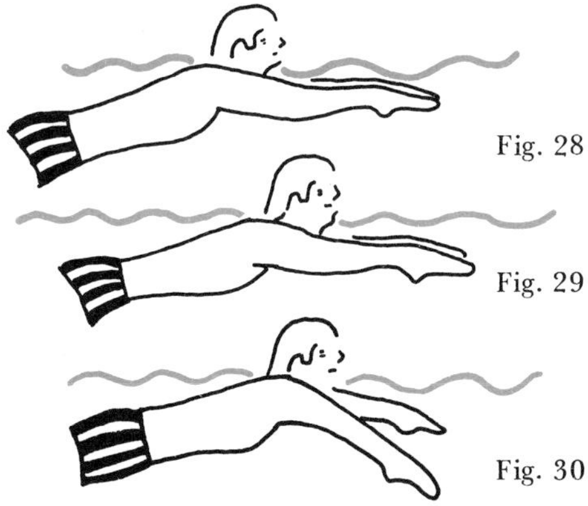

Fig. 28

Fig. 29

Fig. 30

Leg kick:

The leg kick in breast stroke is very important, because swimmers usually get most of their forward movement from the leg kick. In the early stages be content that he can move his feet outwards, backwards and inwards in a circling action. As soon as possible teach him to try this action with his feet turned sideways (Fig. 31a & b).

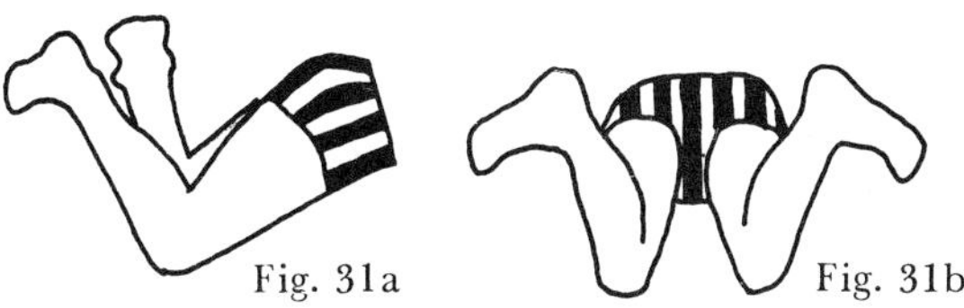

Fig. 31a

Fig. 31b

When kicking, if your child seems unable to turn his feet sideways (in other words he kicks with one or both feet pointed backwards), he will not get much forward movement from it. If this is the case, then he will need to practise the following learning stages so that he learns to kick with flat feet.

1. Hold onto the sides of the pool (rail or trough), and stand with both feet flat on the pool bottom and turned outwards (Fig. 32).

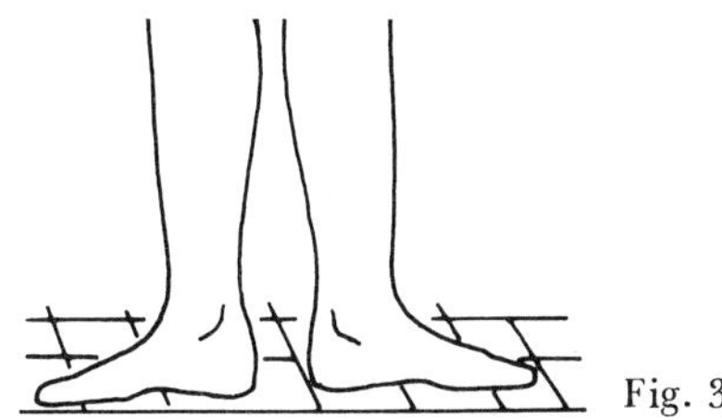

Fig. 32

2. Practise raising both feet off the floor whilst bending his knees. Lower the feet onto the bottom with heels touching first—because he is standing close to the side of the pool, it will be easier for him to raise his feet in a backwards direction (Fig. 33).

Fig. 33

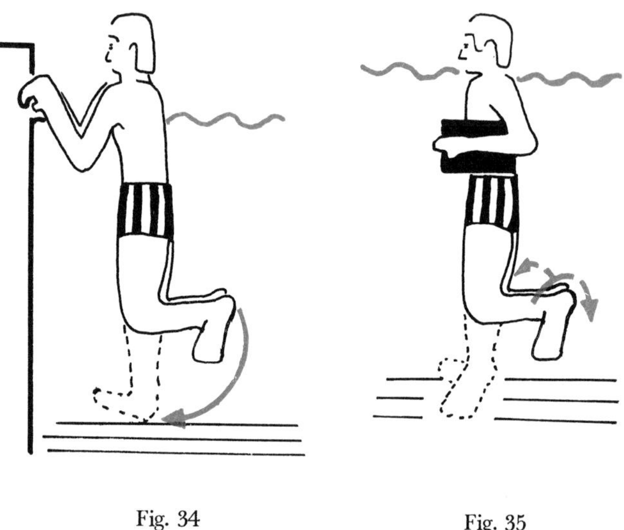
Fig. 34

Fig. 35

3. Practise raising both feet off the pool bottom so that his heels move in a circle with an upward, outward and downwards movement. His feet should be replaced on the pool bottom after each circling movement so that the heels are the first part of the feet to touch the floor (Fig. 34).

4. Hold two floats under each arm and repeat stages 1, 2 and 3, away from the pool side. (Fig. 35)
5. As he develops, there will be no need for him to touch the bottom of the pool with his heels.

Fig. 37.

6. Encourage him to lean forward into a horizontal floating position and practise the kicking action in a backwards direction rather than a downwards direction.

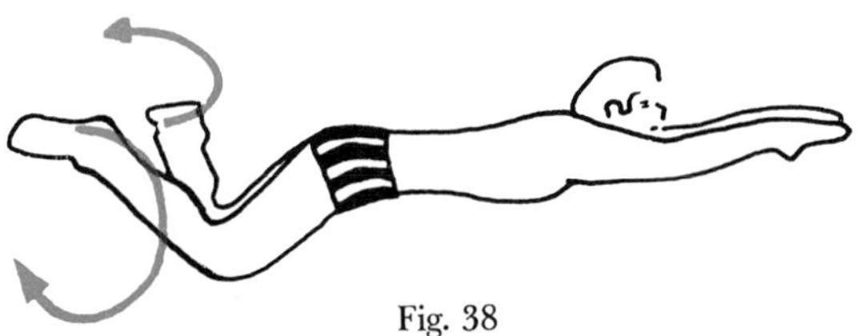

Fig. 38

7. Discard the floats and try swimming with arms and legs. It may be necessary to persevere with these practices as some children have great difficulty learning the correct kick. (Fig. 38)

DEVELOPMENT OF THE BREAST STROKE

As with front crawl children can obtain great benefit from using imaginary aids in the water. First of all get him to lie in the water in a stretched gliding position.

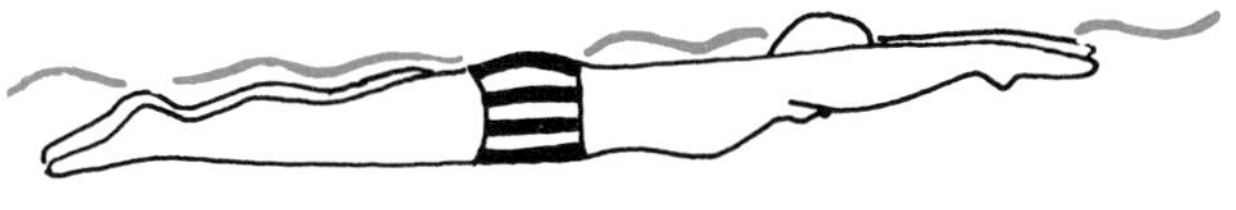

Fig. 39

Now get him to imagine that there are two large hoops about 24″ diameter–one in front and the other behind him.

The one in front lies between his finger tips and his face with the front edge 2″ below the surface, and the rear edge 12″ below the surface. (Fig. 40)

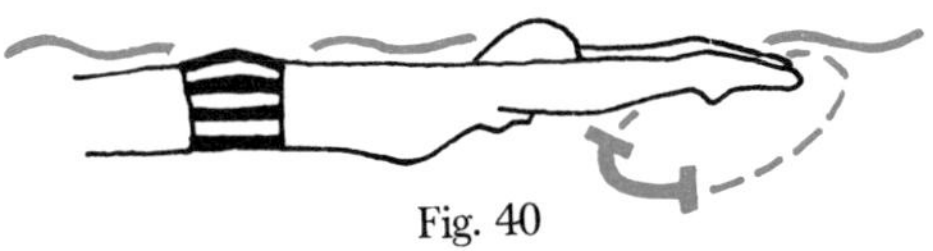

Fig. 40

The second hoop lies between his outstretched feet at a point somewhere between his knees and hips. The near edge is 3″ below the surface and the far edge is approximately 12″ below the surface. (Fig. 41)

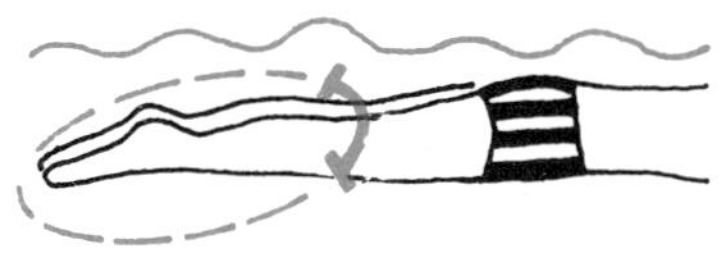

Improvement of body position

When he is swimming the stroke, get him to look at the leading edge of the hoop furthest away from him, except when he is inhaling, then he will raise his head and look forward over the surface of the water.

Arm stroke

His hands and arms which are fully extended start pulling from the leading edge. His little fingers maintain contact and scrape around the inside of the hoop (note his elbows should be higher in the water than his hands throughout this pulling action).

Notice that there is a part of the hoop which is shown in blue. When his hands reach this part, they should come together and move forward along the centre of the hoop, back to the foremost point.

Leg kick

His legs will start from a fully stretched position and bend forwards along the centre of the hoop until they reach the part shown in blue. Up to now his feet will be stretched and his toes will be pointed.

When he reaches the blue mark he should turn his feet sideways as though his toes are touching the inside of the hoop. (Figs. 42a & b). The feet should then be pushed outwards and backwards so that his toes remain touching the hoop until his legs are fully stretched again.

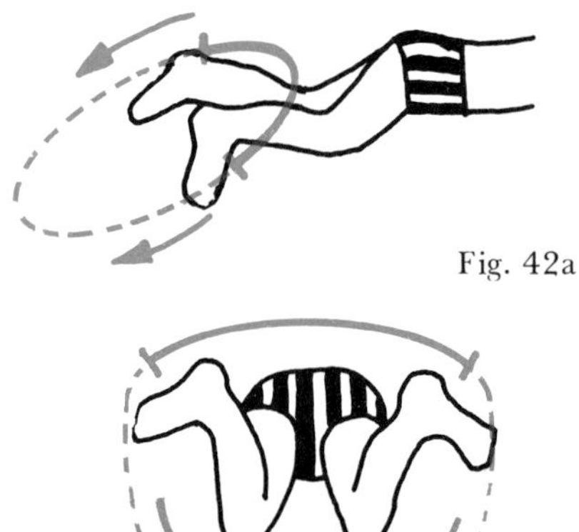

Fig. 42a

Fig. 42b

Breathing

Ideally, inhalation should take place just before the hands reach the part of the hoop shown in blue.

Timing

1. Both arms and legs are touching the outermost edge of the hoop. (Fig. 43).

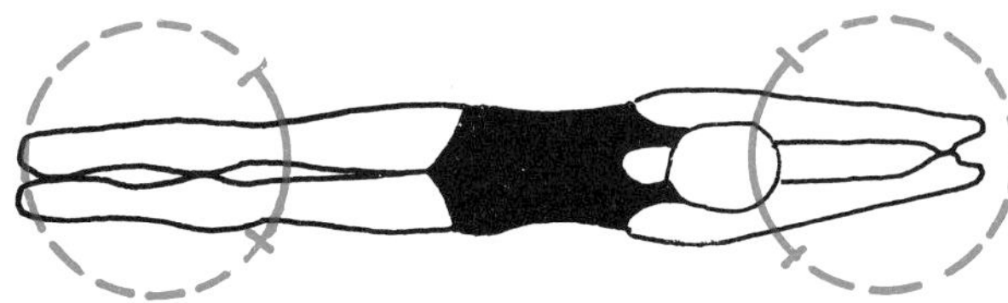

Fig. 43

2. Arms move around hoop–legs remain outstretched. (Fig. 44).

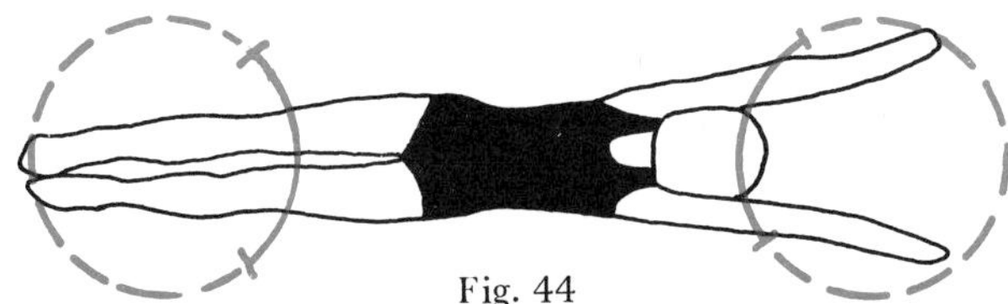

Fig. 44

3. Hands reach blue area–feet move forward across hoop. (Fig. 45)

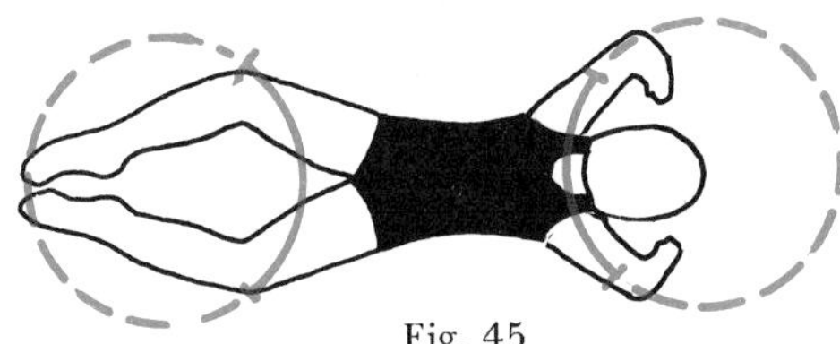

Fig. 45

4. Feet reach blue area and begin to push around the inside of the hoop. Hands come together and move along the centre back to the starting point. (Fig. 46)

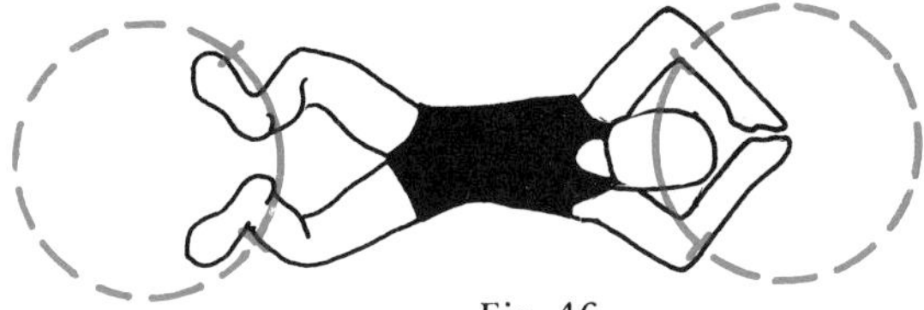

Fig. 46

5. Arms at starting point–feet just finishing pushing around the hoop, until the legs are fully stretched. (Fig. 47)

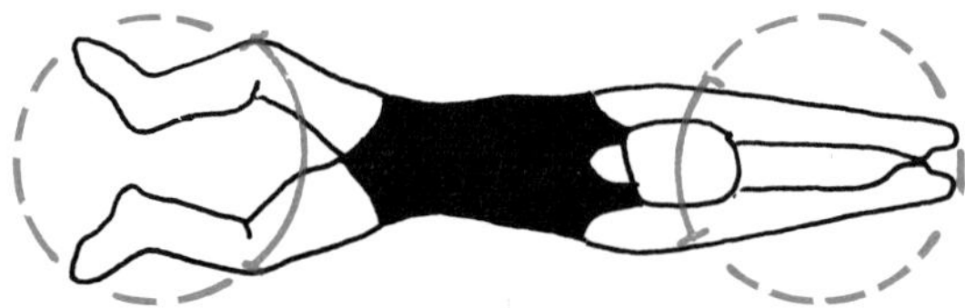

Fig. 47

Fig. 49

The arms and leg movements should be performed smoothly and continuously. Do not rush them.

Fig. 50

MORE ADVANCED PRACTICES

Legs:

Breast stroke kick. Hands hold kick board. (Fig. 48)
Breast stroke kick without kick board—arms in front. (Fig. 49)
Breast stroke kick without kick board—arms by the side. (Fig. 50)
Breast stroke kick—performed on the back. (Fig. 51)

Fig. 51

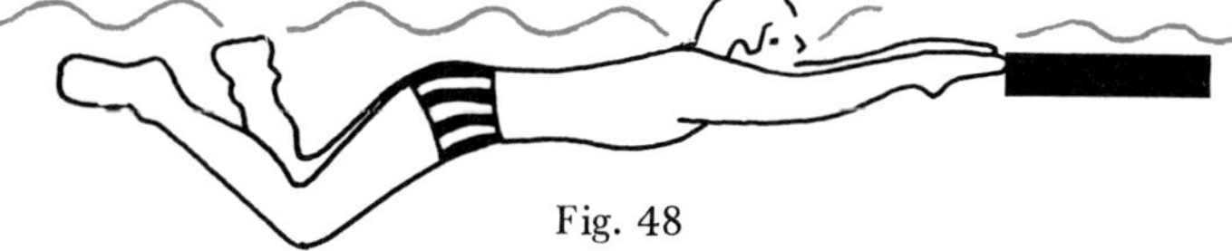

Fig. 48

Arms:

Arms only—pull with float between thighs. (Fig. 52)
Arms only—pull with small dolphin kick. (Fig. 53)

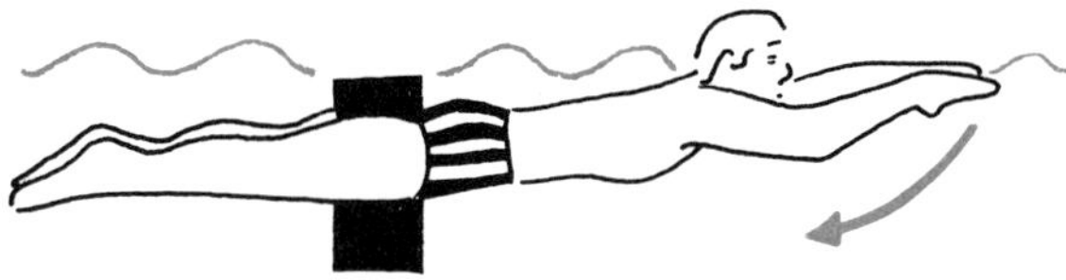

Fig. 52

Fig. 53

BACK STROKE

Back Stroke is the most relaxing of all the swimming strokes because breathing is easier.

When you get tired you can keep moving by resting your arms alongside your body and maintain your leg kick. In this way, even a poor swimmer can swim long distances.

There are many different ways of swimming on the back as there are various ways of swimming on the front.

1. *Back Crawl*—your arms pull alternately, whilst your legs kick up and down. (Fig. 54)

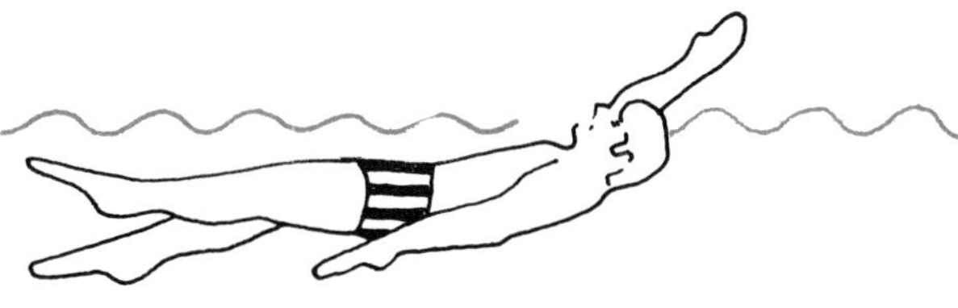

Fig 54

2. *Back Breast Stroke*—the arms pull simultaneously through the water and the legs kick simultaneously in circles. (Fig. 55)

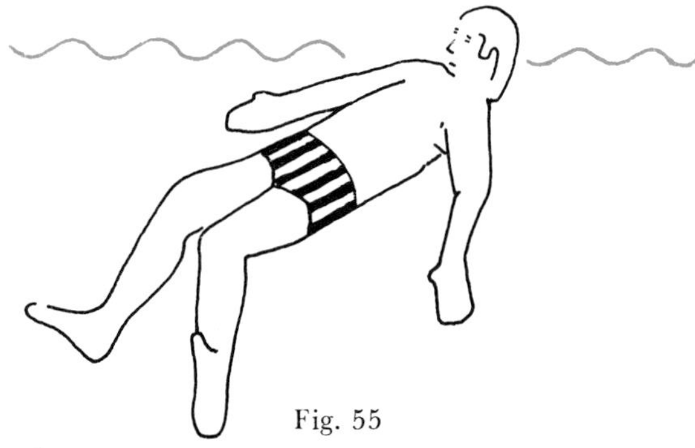
Fig. 55

3. The arms can be recovered over the water as described for Back Dolphin and the legs kick simultaneously in circles. This is sometimes referred to as the Old English Back Stroke. See arm action Fig. 56 and leg action Fig. 55.
4. *Back Dolphin Stroke*—the arms pull simultaneously (arms recover over the water) whilst the legs kick simultaneously in an up and down movement.(Fig.56)

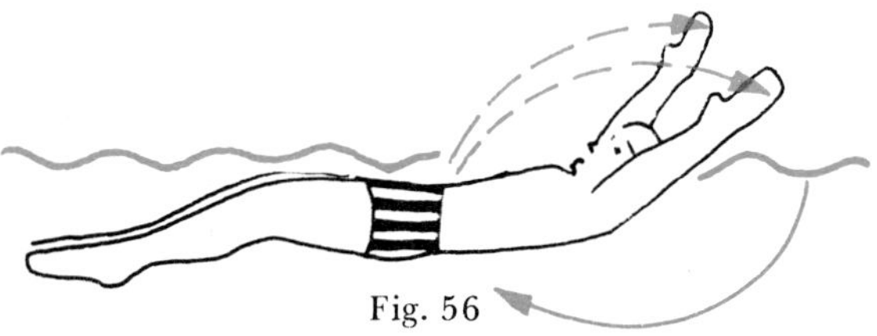
Fig. 56

INITIAL LEARNING STAGES FOR ALL BACK STROKES

Body position

To enable your child to swim well on his back, he must learn how to obtain a good body position.

He should be looking upwards and his 'tummy' should be near the surface (Fig. 57).

Fig. 57.

As he floats in this way, he should try to kick up and down with his legs (Fig. 59).

As soon as possible encourage him to try without the aid of floats, performing a sculling action with his hands.

To help him learn sculling, get him to imagine there are two large upturned saucers submerged approximately 2″ under the water alongside his hips, and then tell him to stroke his hands from side to side over the backs of the saucers (Figs. 58 & 118a, b, c).

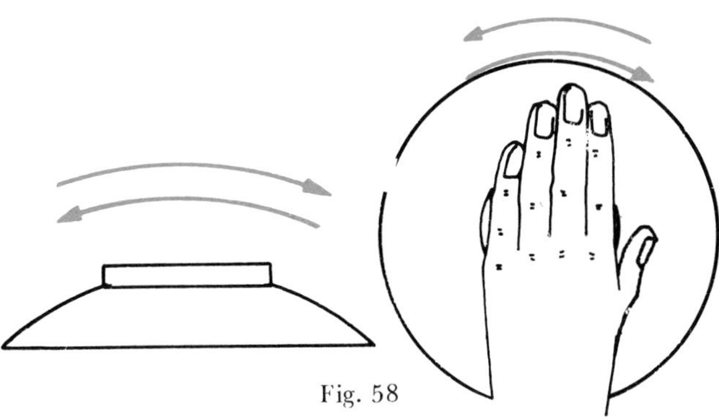
Fig. 58

Leg kick—back crawl

He can practise the back crawl kick in the same way as for front crawl. Let him imagine that there is a kicking board ½″ away from his fully stretched feet. He should kick alternately upwards and downwards so that he touches the underneath of the board with the tops of his feet on the upward movement. This will help him to extend his feet. (Fig. 59).

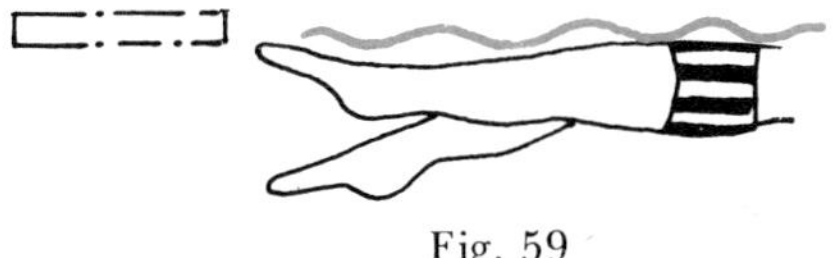
Fig. 59

Back breast

He can develop the leg kick in the same way as he did for ordinary breast stroke (Figs. 42a, b, page 52). His feet move in an outward, backward and inward action, so that his toes maintain contact with the inside of the hoop except for the area coloured in blue. (Fig. 60)

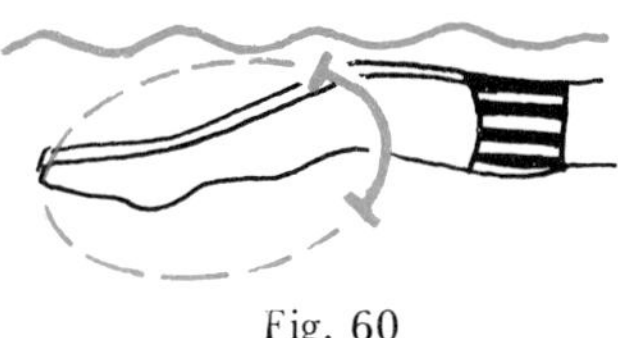
Fig. 60

Back dolphin

The dolphin leg kick is the same as for alternating back crawl, except the legs kick together. The imaginary kicking board can be used again (Fig. 61).

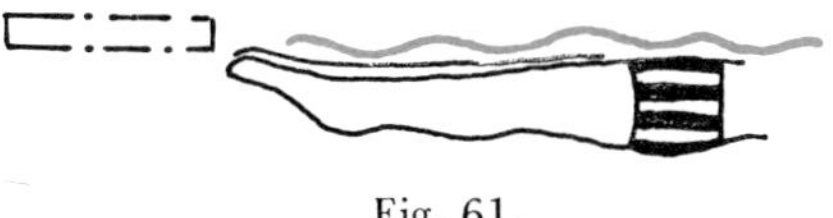
Fig. 61.

The most popular stroke of those mentioned is the back crawl. It is faster than the others, although it is not as relaxing as back breast stroke.

TEACHING A SIMPLE BACK CRAWL

Both the body position and leg kick of back crawl have been explained.

Arm action:

Imagination can help a great deal in the initial stages of learning the arm action. The diagram shows two half hoops. One half hoop is vertically out of the water and the other horizontally under the surface. The shoulder is the central point (Fig. 62). Imagine these hoops on both sides of the body.

When your child recovers his hand and arm out of the water, his hand leaves the water at his thigh. Get him to stretch his arm so that the tips of his fingers touch the inside of the vertical imaginary hoop and then move along the hoop maintaining contact until his hand enters the water beyond his head. Try to ensure that the little finger enters the water first.

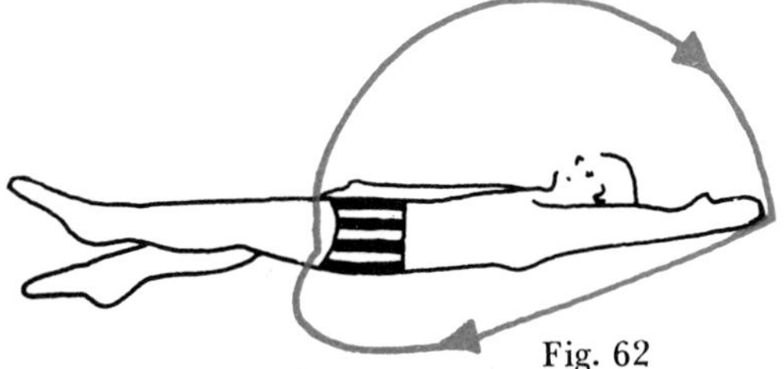

Fig. 62

This hand which has just entered the water then swings horizontally so that his fingers follow the hoop round to the thigh. (Fig. 63).

His hand and wrist should be held firm so that he can hold onto the water.

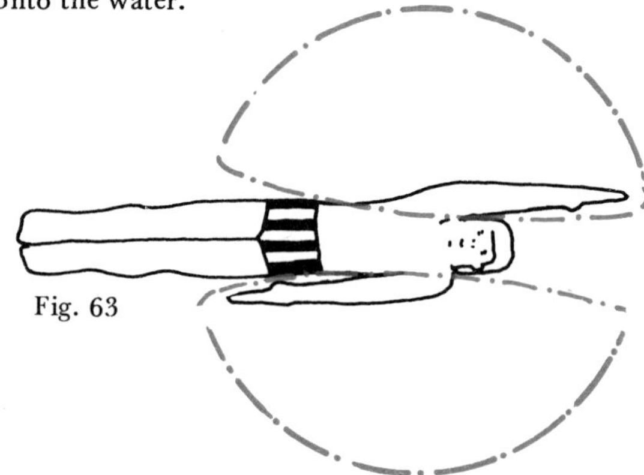

Fig. 63

His other hand should follow the same pathway using hoops on the other side of the body. The hands however, should be at opposite positions on the hoops, i.e. if his left hand is halfway along the vertical hoop, his right hand should be halfway along the horizontal hoop.

Development of back crawl

Usually the legs kick six times to one complete arm cycle. This applies whether it is swum by a beginner or a good swimmer.

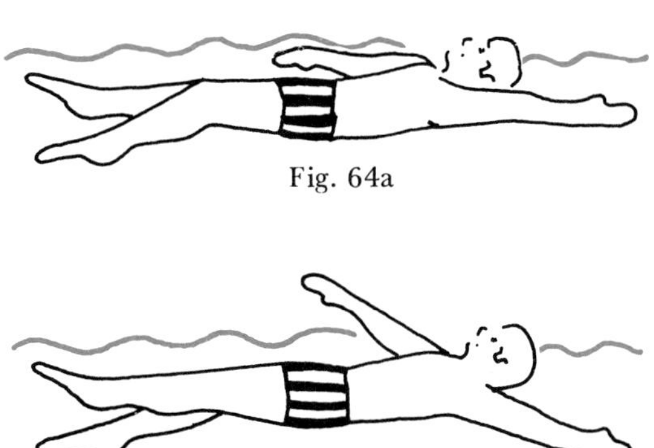

Fig. 64a

Fig. 64b

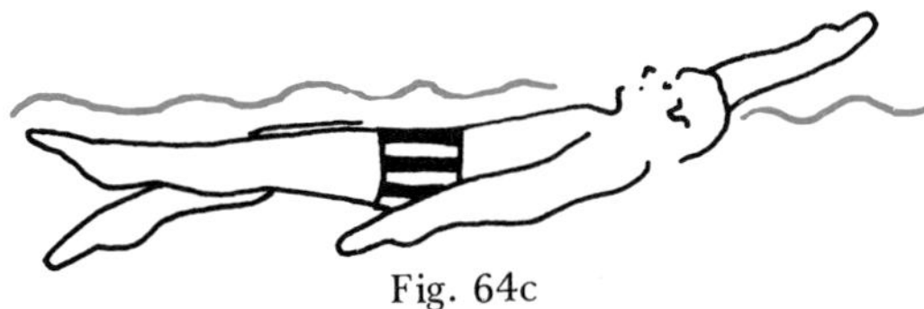

Fig. 64c

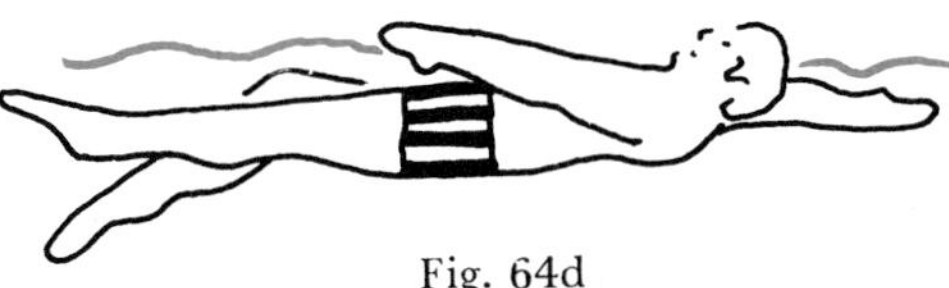

Fig. 64d

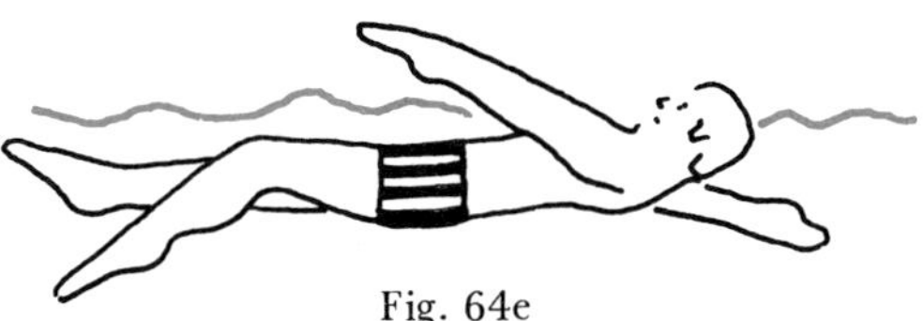

Fig. 64e

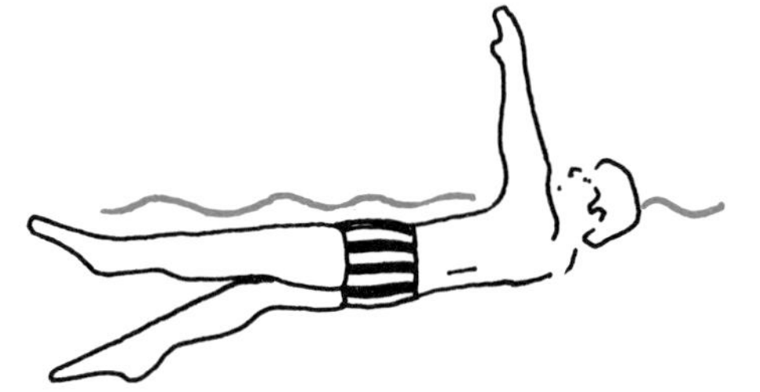

Fig. 64f

Up to now your child will have been swimming back crawl with straight arms throughout the overwater and underwater movements (Figs. 64a-f). Another way, yet faster to swim back crawl, is for him to bend his arms as he is pulling under water (some children can do this naturally from the beginning). (Figs. 65a-f).

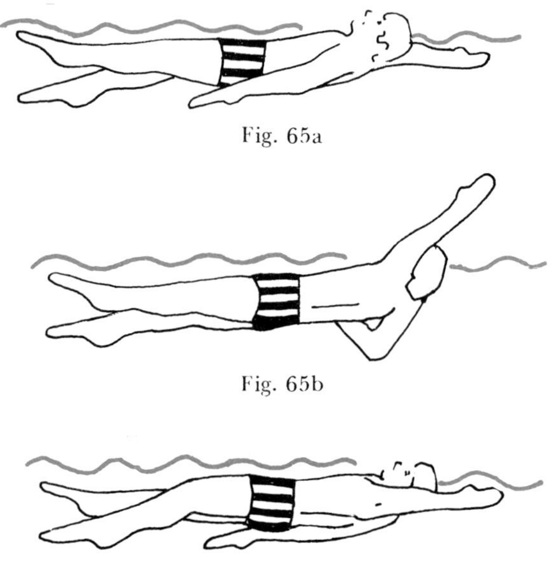

Fig. 65a

Fig. 65b

Fig. 65c

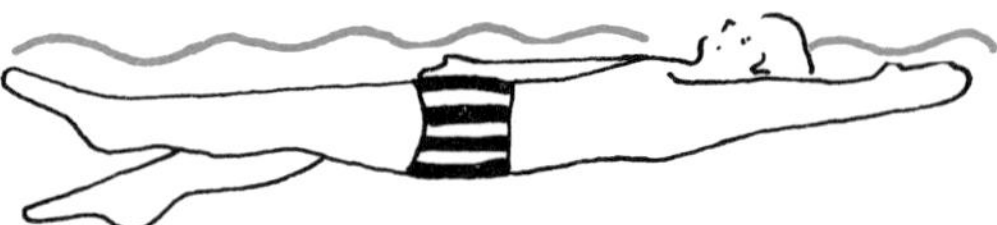

Fig. 65d

Fig. 65e

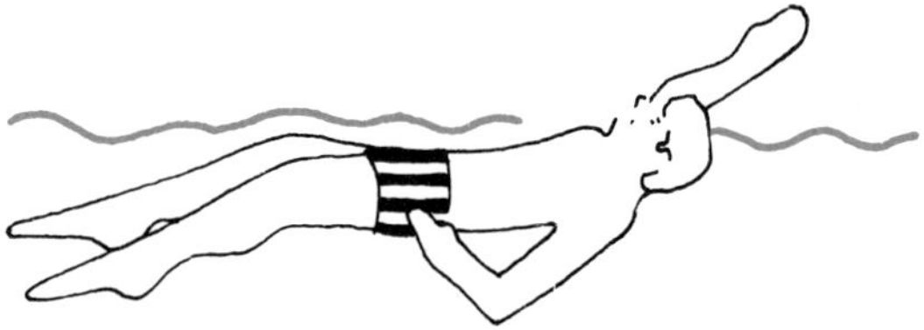

Fig. 65f

Whilst you are trying to get him to develop a bent arm pull, suggest that when his hand reaches a point along the horizontal hoop, level with his shoulder, he should start to turn the palm of his hand over (Fig. 65e). It will only be fully turned over, i.e. palm of his hand facing the bottom of the pool when it reaches a point about 9″ below the level of his thigh (Fig. 65e).

When he can do this, encourage him to bend his arm more and pull closer to the body.

Some children develop this action when they work both arms simultaneously as in Back Dolphin.

When your child is competent at swimming with bent arms, the path of his hand will be following an 'S' shape. (Fig. 66).

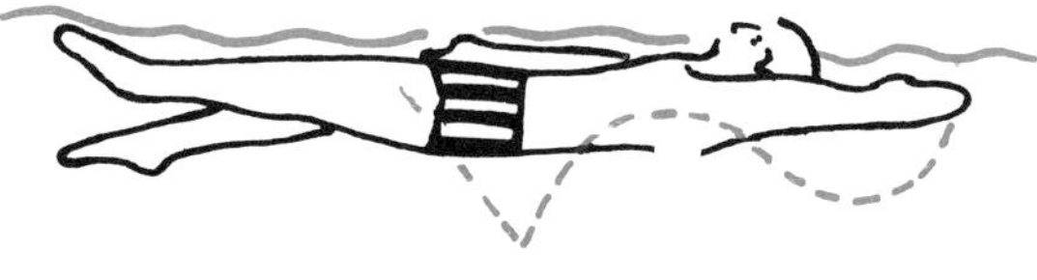

Fig. 66.

MORE ADVANCED PRACTICES

Kicking:

Back flutter–kick with one arm extended beyond head, the other at the side. (Fig. 67)

Back flutter–kick with both arms extended beyond head.
Back flutter–kick with quarter turn of the body onto the side.

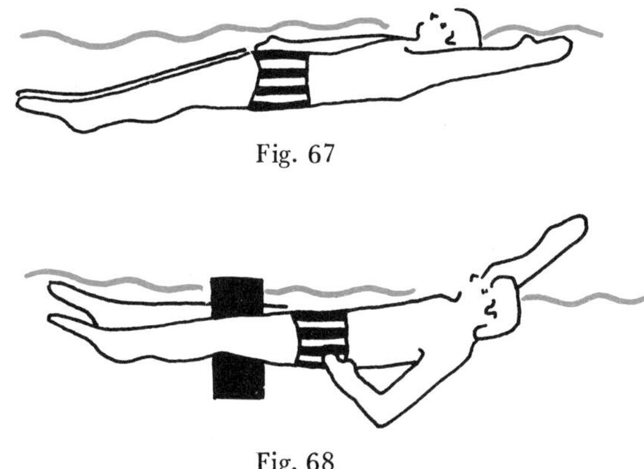

Fig. 67

Fig. 68

Arms only–with kick board held at the thigh (Fig. 68).
Arms only–legs dragging.
Single arm–pulls with one arm by side.
Single arm–pulls with other arm extended beyond head.
Variations of arm pulling three times with one arm then three times with the other arm.
Swim with hand paddles.

Coordination

Back flutter kick and arm action, but pause three seconds when arm enters beyond head and before the pull commences.
Gradually reduce the length of this pause.

BUTTERFLY STROKE

This can be the most difficult of all the strokes to learn and is the most tiring.

Some children find the butterfly stroke easy and therefore should be encouraged to swim it in the early learning stages. More success however will be gained if time is spent in acquiring competence in the other strokes especially front crawl before attempting the complete butterfly stroke.

Learning the Butterfly can be achieved by setting out to obtain a proficient leg action before attempting coordination of the arms with the legs. Other children may find it better to begin with the arm action allowing the legs to develop naturally within the stroke.

Leg kick

Kick deep and powerfully. This will keep his hips up. Try holding a kicking board in front at arms length (Fig. 69a, b, c).

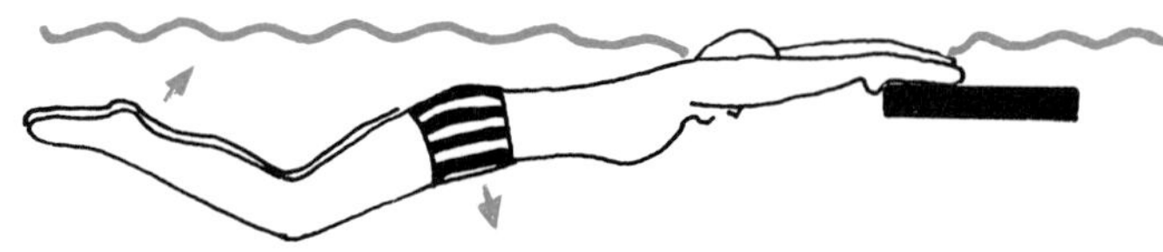

Fig. 69a

Get him to perform an up and down eel-like movement, of the trunk and legs, first with his hands by his side and then with them extended in front of him. (Fig. 70).

Suggest that he tries it under water and he will be amazed how well he will be able to move.

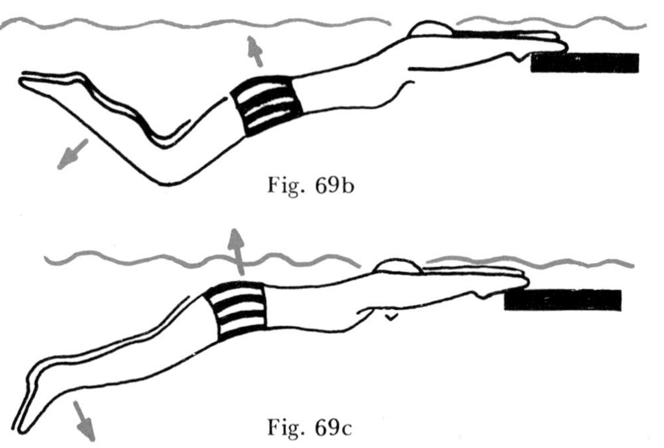

Fig. 69b

Fig. 69c

When he can progress in this dolphin manner then is the time to add the arms. Do not bother about breathing at this stage. The complete stroke is illustrated Figs. 71a-e.

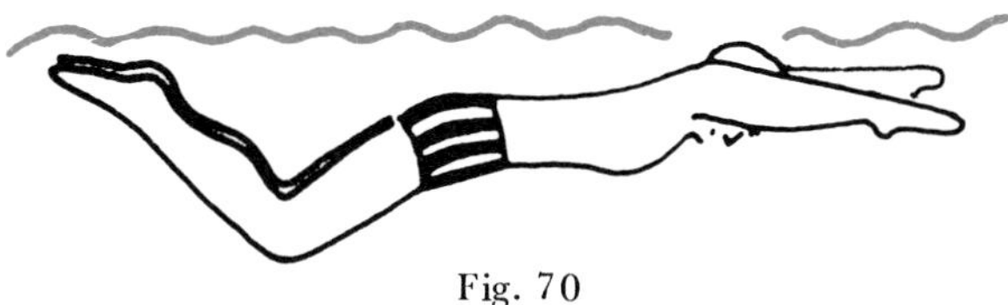

Fig. 70

If he experiences difficulty practising the arm movement when he is swimming, let him practise it as he is walking across the pool.

It may help him to recover his arms in the water at first, i.e. swim dolphin kicking, using the normal arm pull under water but pushing the arms forward close to the body underwater, and then back to full extension. It may also help if he swims with a float held at the thigh.

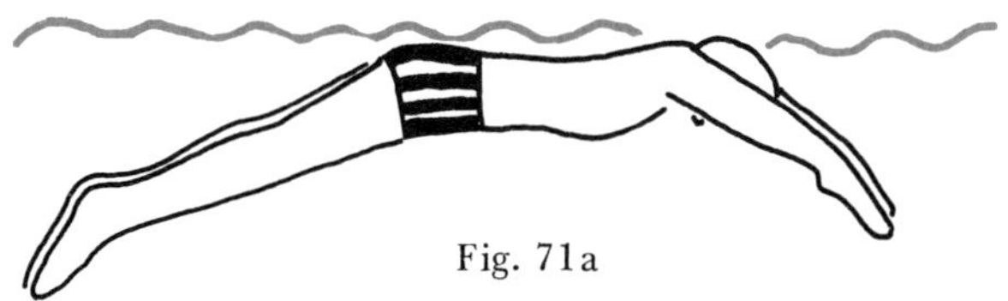

Fig. 71a

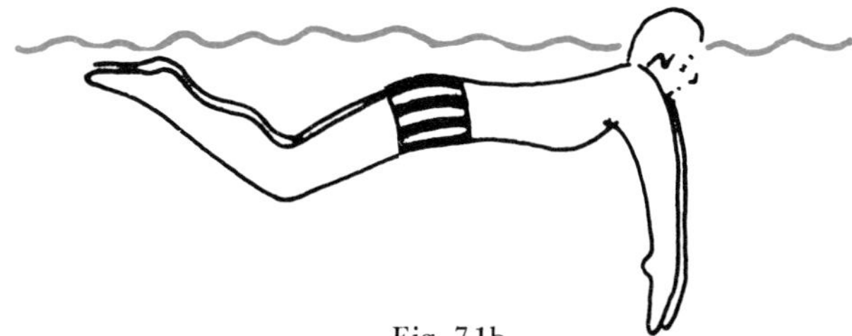

Fig. 71b

Fig. 71c

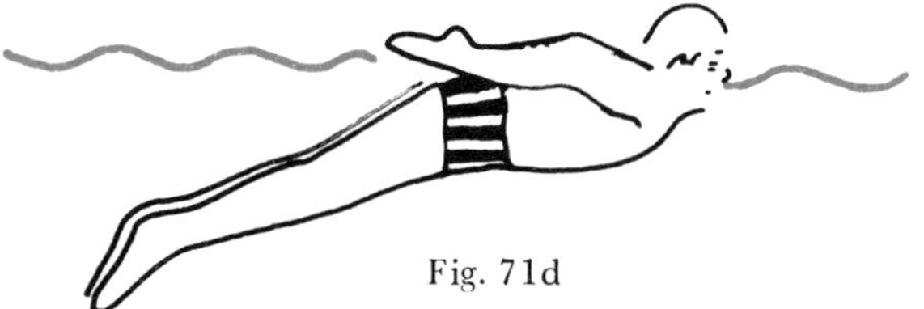

Fig. 71d

Fig. 71e

Some children find that they can swim butterfly arm action combined with a breast stroke leg kick. Although they appear quite successful, this should not be encouraged if you wish your child to take part in competitive swimming.

MORE ADVANCED PRACTICES

Kick:

Butterfly dolphin on the side.
One leg butterfly kick.
Use flippers (Fig. 72).

Fig. 72

Arms:

Butterfly arms without legs.
One arm butterfly opposite arm extended. (Fig. 73)
Use hand paddles. (Fig. 74)

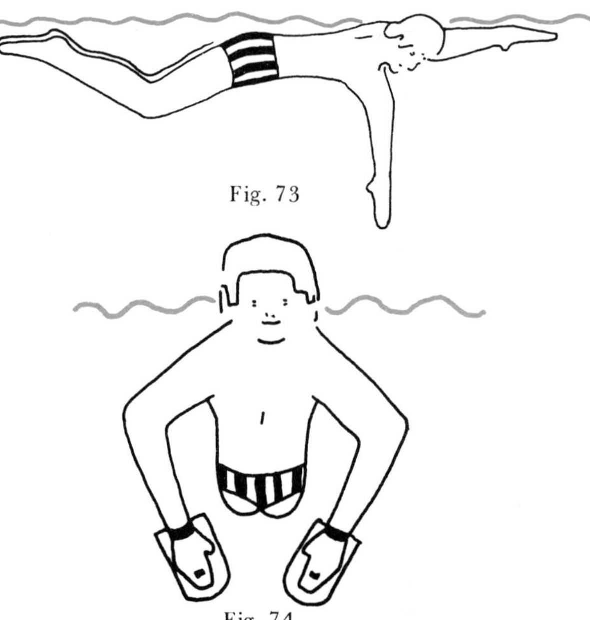

Fig. 73

Fig. 74

Part 3
Other Skills

Diving (First Stages)
Starts and Turns for Racing
Survival
Sculling
Ball Skills
Other Diving Skills

DIVING

The first practices for diving will have been done early on when you were encouraging your child in the early confidence practices.

The following activities are useful:

a. Hand standing (Fig. 75)

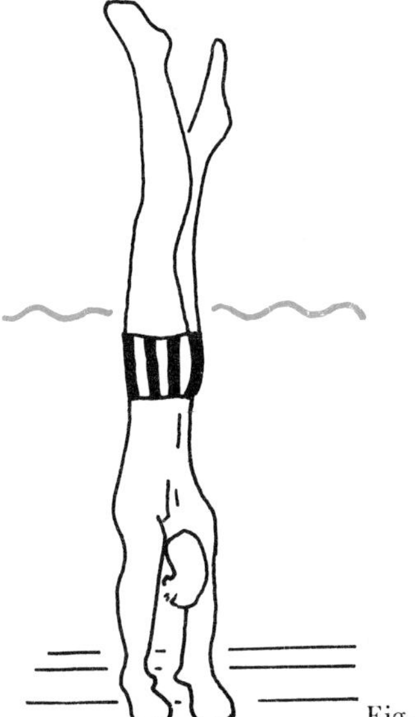

Fig. 75

b. Gliding (Fig. 76)

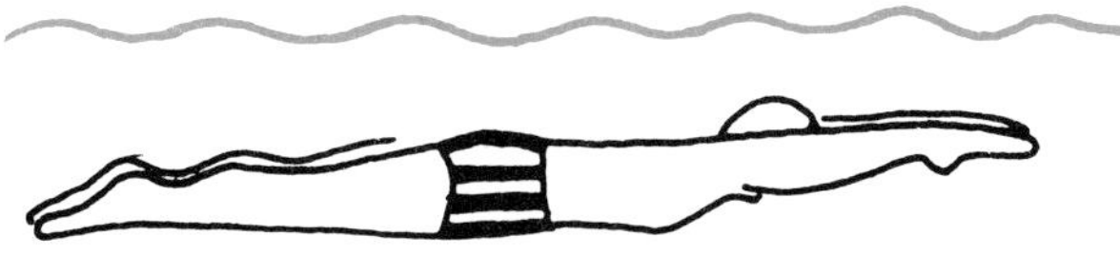

Fig. 76

c. Gliding through other peoples' legs (Fig. 77) or looking for and picking up objects from the bottom.

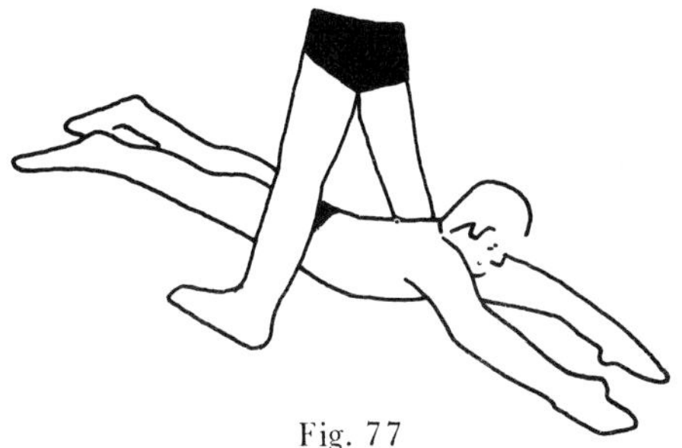

Fig. 77

d. Picking objects up off the floor of the pool. (Fig. 78)

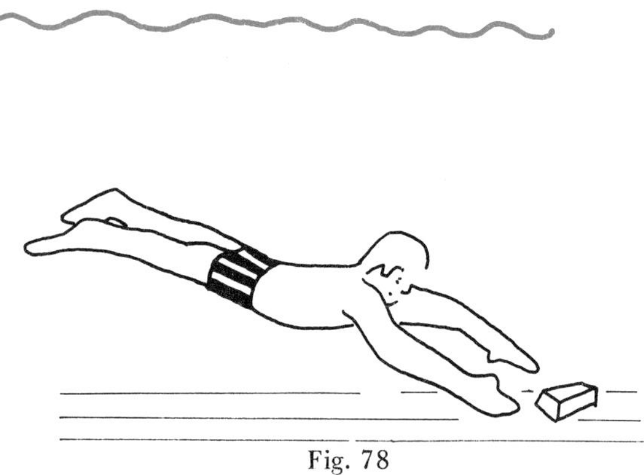

Fig. 78

These activities will help him to keep his eyes open underneath the water and will teach him how to return to the surface.

If the pool you are using has steps and your child is able to sit lower in the water than he would on the poolside, he can commence with a sitting dive (Fig. 79).

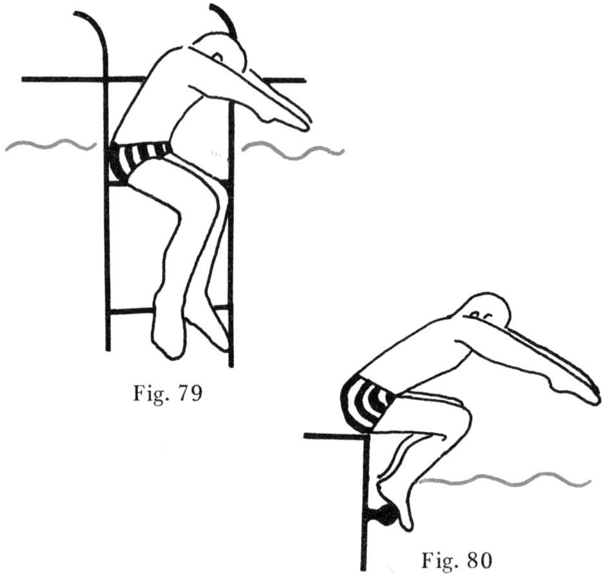

Fig. 79

Fig. 80

Crouch with his body between his knees. His arms are stretched forward—hands together. Get him to press his upper arm into his ears.

Next practice is a sitting dive from the poolside with his feet on the rail or scum trough. (Fig. 80).

Now get him to squat with his toes wrapped over the edge. He should overbalance and stretch as he enters the water and he should try to bring his legs together.

Fig. 81

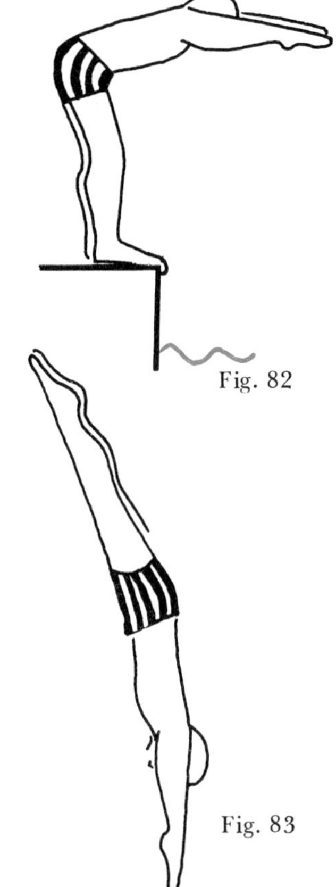

Fig. 82

Fig. 83

He should now be gaining confidence and will be able to straighten his legs a little more. His hands will be joined above his head. Get him now to spring out into the water more (Fig. 81).

A word of caution!—now that he is getting higher, make sure that the water is deep enough. If he is diving from the bathside, the water should be deeper than your child's full height plus his stretched arm length.

Now get him to dive without bending his knees on the initial stance. Suggest that he imagines there is a pole in front of his hips and his lower legs must pass over this Fig. 82. If he does this correctly, he will make a near vertical entry (Fig. 83).

When he attempts a racing dive, his stance on the pool side will be the same for all strokes except back crawl (see page 74 Fig. 90).

He will place his feet about hip width apart, his toes will be curled over the edge and his knees will be slightly bent. His arms will point downwards and slightly forwards and his eyes will look about halfway along the pool. (Fig. 84)

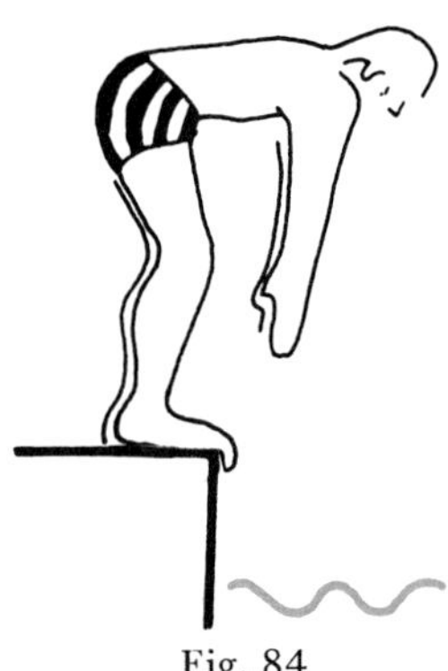

Fig. 84

When he first tries racing dives, encourage him to throw himself forward vigorously. His body should be stretched and streamlined with his head between his arms, Fig. 85.

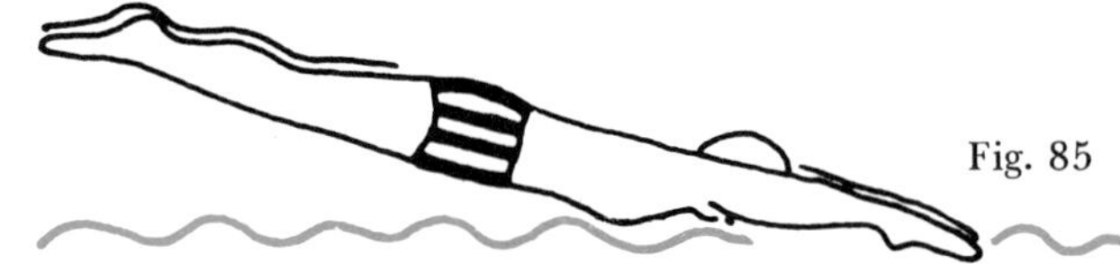

Fig. 85

Make sure that he stretches on entry and glides before coming to the surface. The first stroke after the start in breast stroke is rather special and is explained in detail on pages 73-74, Figs. 89a-d.

Soon he will need to synchronise the arm movements with the leg drive. Get him to practise swinging his arms forwards, sideways, backwards and forwards again. (He may have to practice this on land before attempting the dive.)

Now practise the stance and entry. (Figs. 86a-g and photos pages 77 & 78).

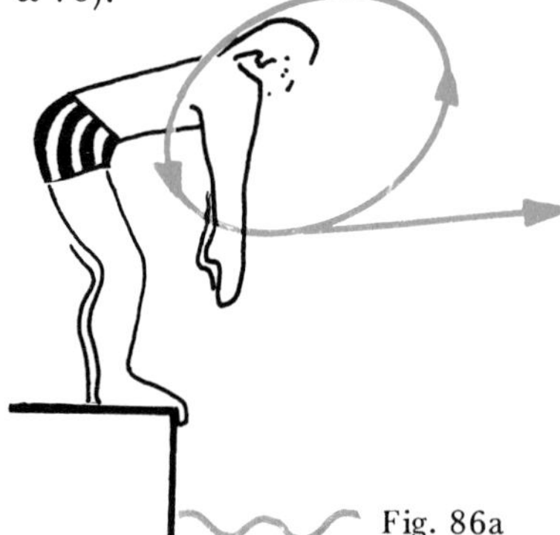

Fig. 86a

Fig. 86b

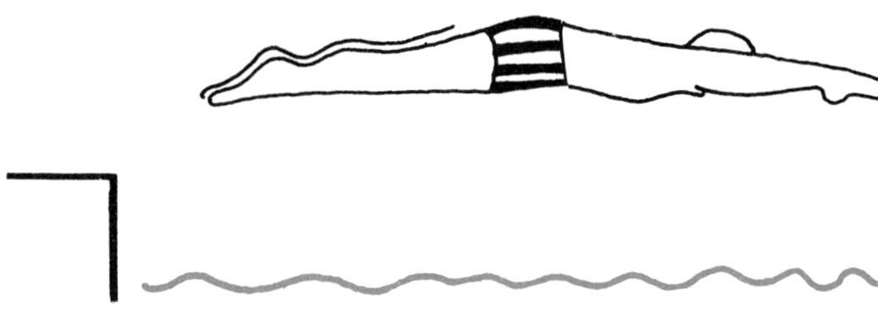
Fig. 86e

When he starts front crawl he should dive, stretch, glide—kick—pull one arm and he should then be at the surface. (Figs. 87a, b, c and photos pages 77 & 78).

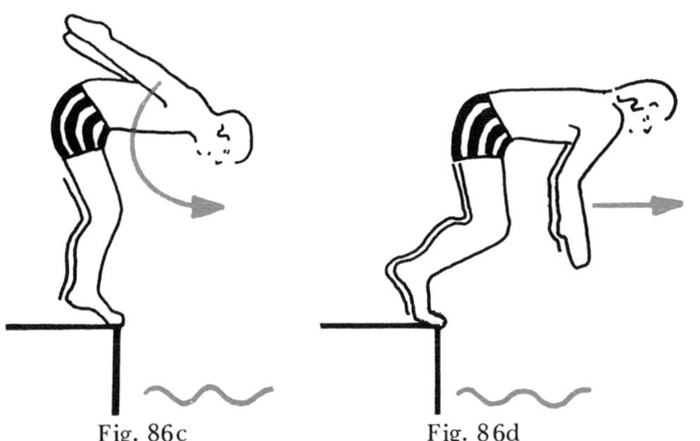
Fig. 86c

Fig. 86d

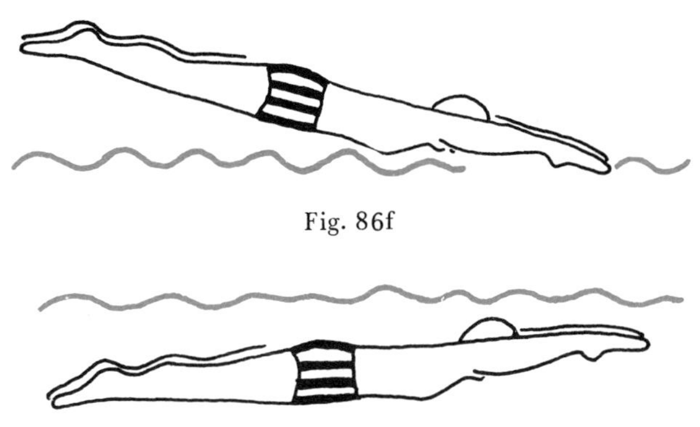
Fig. 86f

Fig. 86g

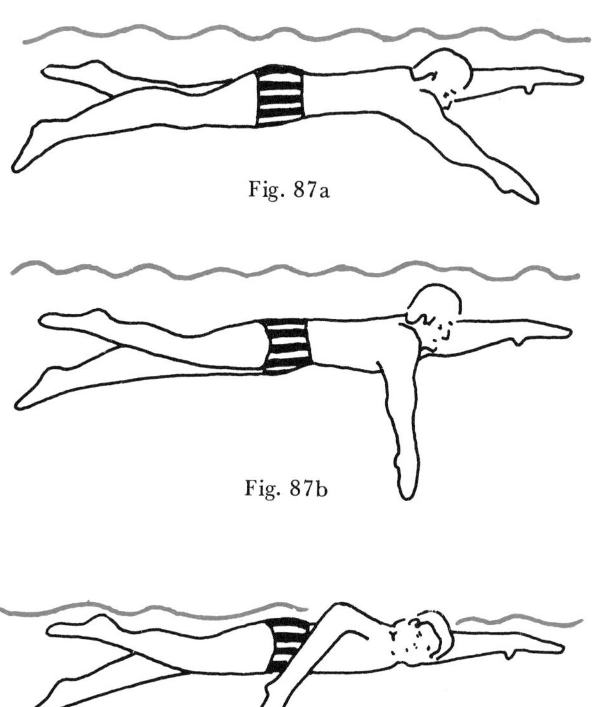
Fig. 87a

Fig. 87b

Fig. 87c

When he starts butterfly, he should dive—stretch, glide, kick—pull with two arms and he should then be at the surface (Figs. 88a-f).

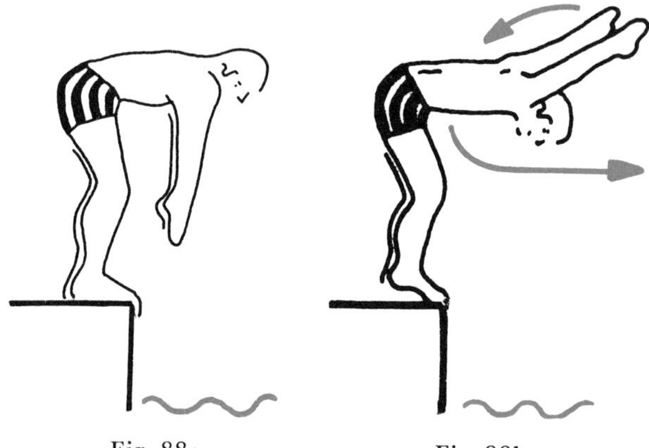
Fig. 88a

Fig. 88b

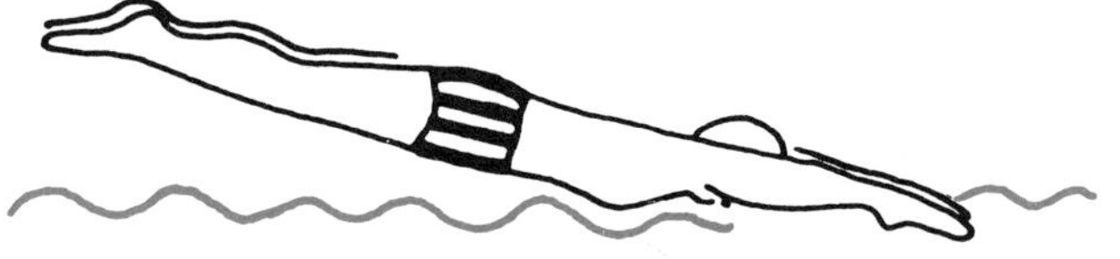
Fig. 88c

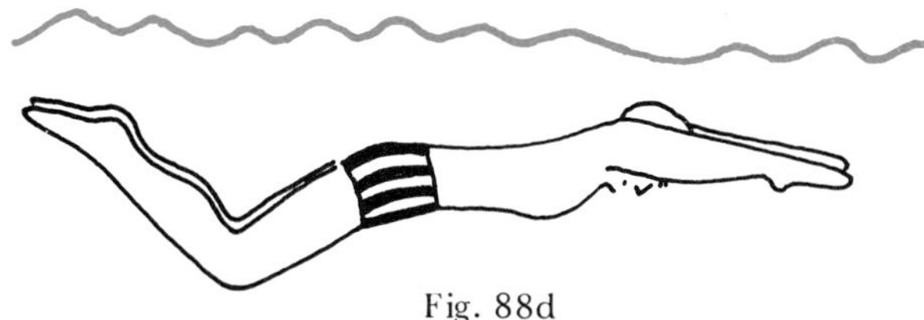

Fig. 88d

Fig. 88e

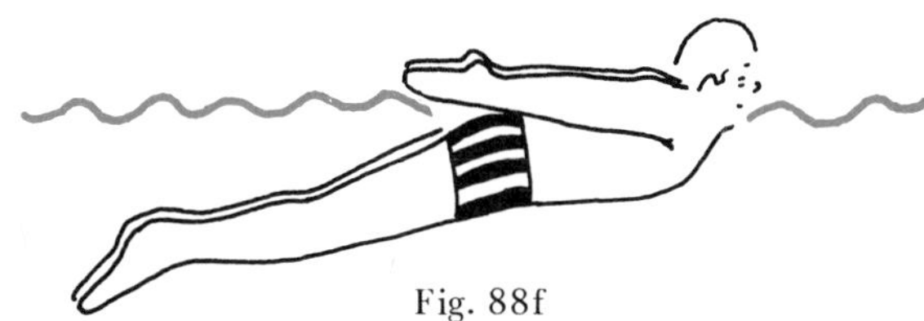

Fig. 88f

When he starts breast stroke he should dive a little deeper—stretch—glide Fig. 89a—pull with both arms Fig. 89b—glide Fig. 89c--kick with both legs Fig. 89d and then he should reach the surface with arms stretched forward.

The breast stroke pull, at the start, is special in that the arms commence their pull from a position which is fully stretched in front of the body and continue as far back as the thighs (Figs. 89a-c). (Practise underwater swimming using this long pulling action.)

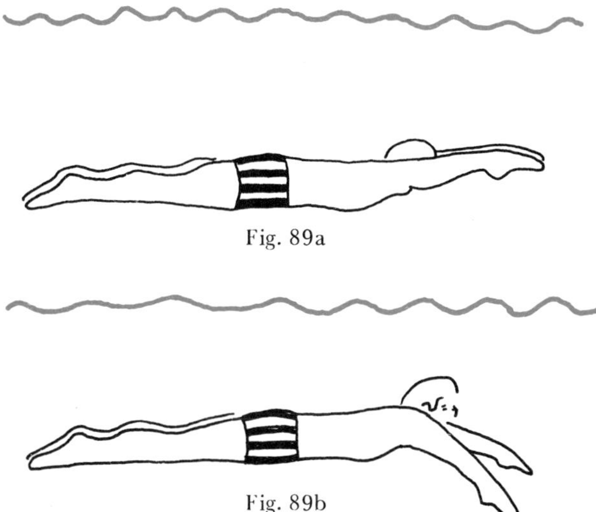

Fig. 89a

Fig. 89b

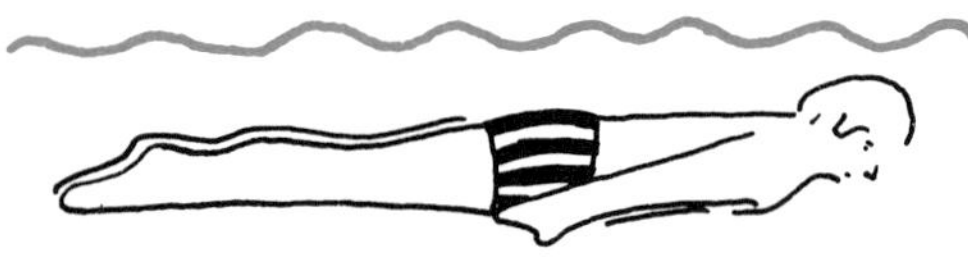

Fig. 89c

The leg kick is normal. The hands are returned forward to the front as close to the body as possible while gliding to the surface (Fig. 89d).

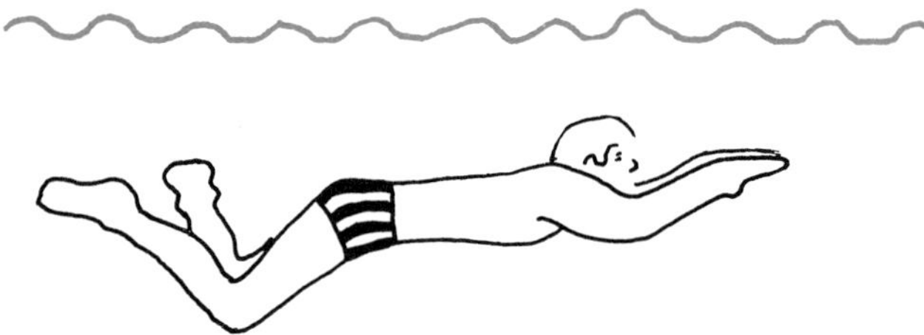

Fig. 89d

His hands should not start another pull stroke until his head breaks the surface.

Back stroke start

This start commences in the water. His hands hold the starting rail with his feet firmly on the wall just under the surface. His knees will be fully bent (Fig. 90).

Fig. 90

When he starts from the wall, he must push hard with his hands first of all, then his feet, so that he tries to skim over the water. (If he does not get most of his body out of the water it will be a very slow start.)

His hands swing past his head sideways, backwards and into a fully-stretched position. (Figs. 91 b,c)

When he enters the water, his body should stretch, then he should kick his feet vigorously (Fig. 91d).

The first arm stroke is taken with one arm, the second stroke must be taken when he has come to the surface. (Fig. 91e)

Fig. 91a

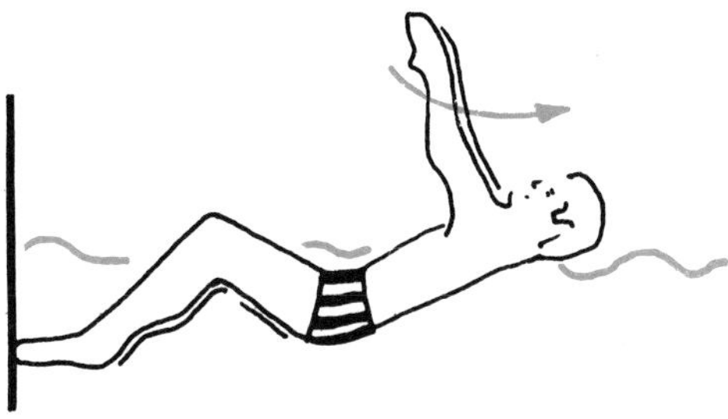

Fig. 91b

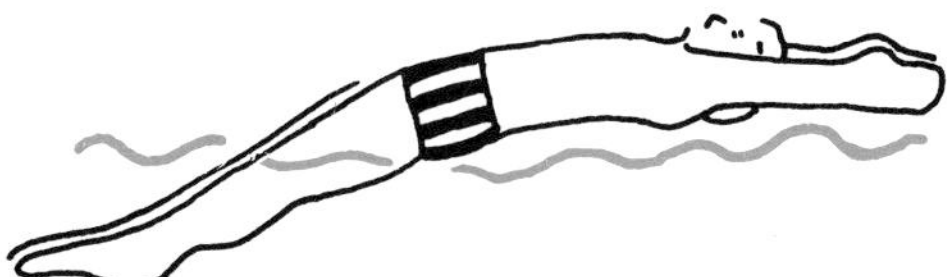

Fig. 91c

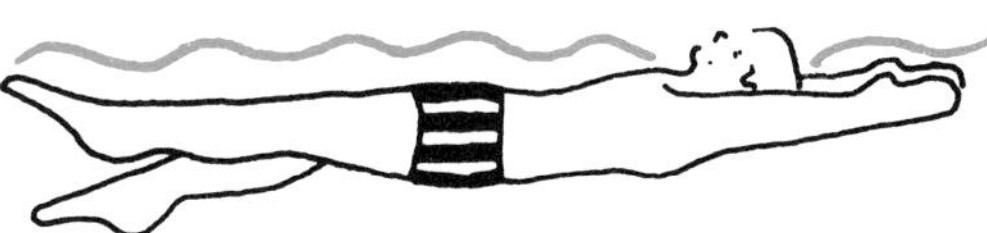

Fig. 91d

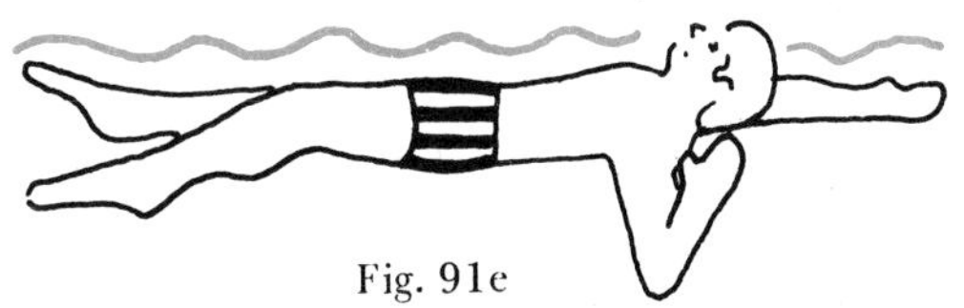

Fig. 91e

Front crawl turn

There are many ways of turning whilst swimming front crawl. The important point to realise in racing is that there is no need to touch the wall with your hand, as long as some part of the body touches.

The quickest turn is a tumble turn which is simply half a forward somersault with a small twist of the body. (Figs. 92a-e)

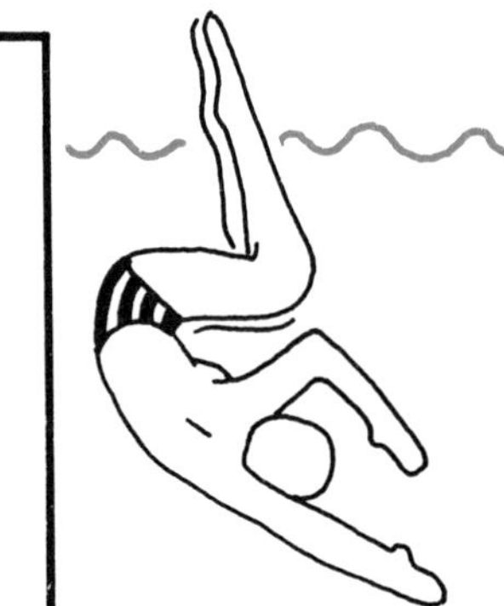

Fig. 92b

Fig. 92a

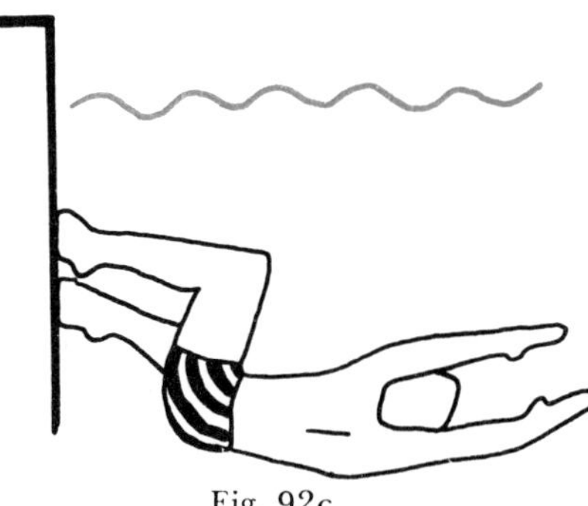

Fig. 92c

Learning a tumble turn

It is important therefore, that before you encourage your child to perform a tumble turn, he should be given the opportunity of practising front somersaults. For this he must have his chin on his chest and his head must not twist sideways.

When he can do this, let him practise half somersaults onto the end wall. He will arrive with his feet on the wall in this position: (Fig. 93).

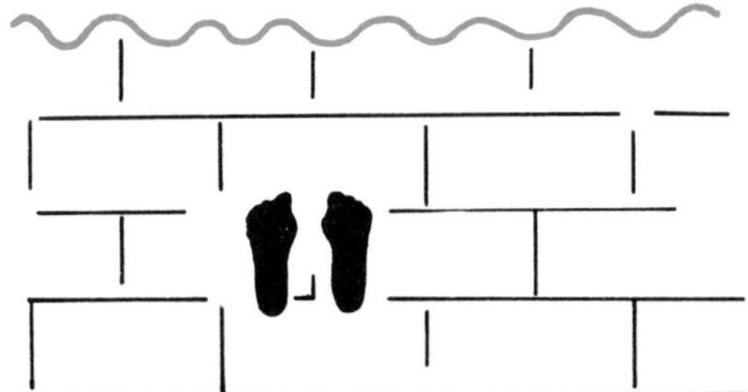

Fig. 93

Get him to practise pushing off from the wall from this position so that he has to twist round to get onto his front.

It is not difficult now to encourage a little turning movement after the half somersault so that his feet arrive on the wall in this position: (Fig. 94).

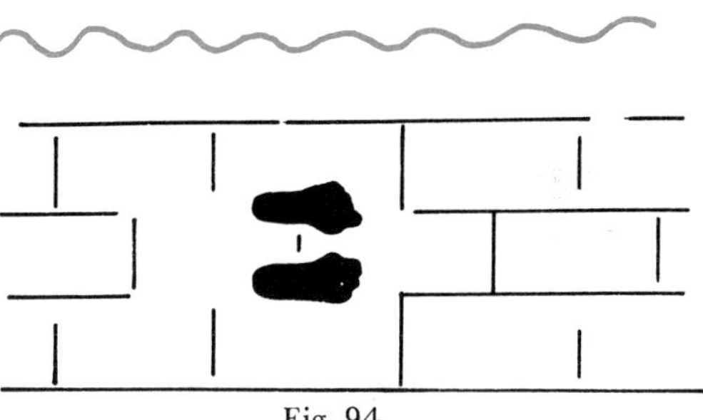

Fig. 94

He will now not have so far to twist onto his front.

Breast stroke and butterfly turns

It is essential for anyone who is a competitor to practise touching the end wall with both hands simultaneously. The hands must touch at the same level (Figs. 95-96a).

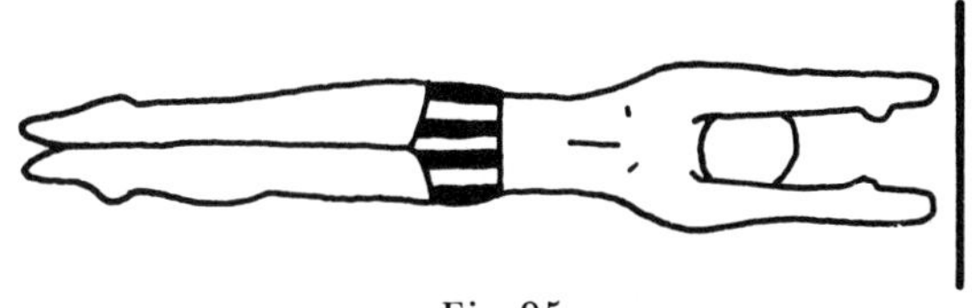

Fig. 95

Fig. 96a

Fig. 96b

After touching the wall he should tuck his legs up so that they are ready to be placed on the wall for a vigorous push off (Fig. 96b).

One hand pushes away from the wall whilst the other pulls on the water helping to turn the body round (Fig. 96c).

Fig. 96c

The push off is forceful and streamlined. The breast stroke push off should be slightly deeper so that one arm stroke and one leg stroke can be performed underwater before coming to the surface. This is shown in the breast stroke start on pages 73-74.

Back crawl turn

Make sure that your child's hand touches the end wall whilst he is still swimming on his back, when he is performing this turn (Fig. 102).

The racing turn which is called a flip or pivot turn requires him to lift his lower legs out of the water and twist them round to touch the end wall ready for a push off in the opposite direction (Figs. 103, 104).

This turn can be practised first of all without taking the feet out of the water which makes it easier to perform, but much slower in execution.

Teaching a simple back crawl turn

1. Teach the push off from the end wall. His knees should be well bent as he pushes through the water. Make the push off shallow. His hands do not come out of the water but slide past, close to his face, until they reach full extension beyond his head (Fig. 97).

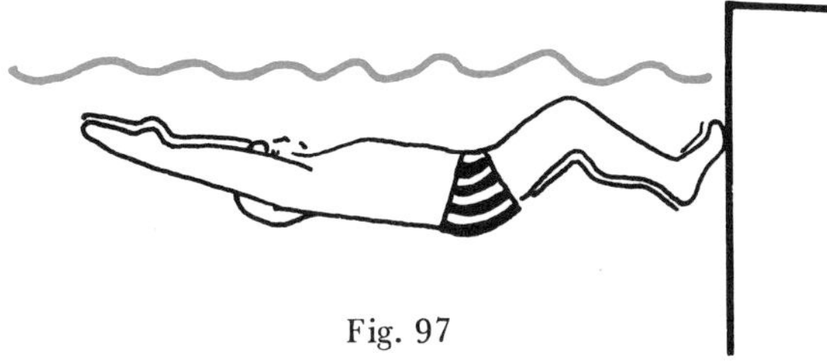

Fig. 97

2. Have him practise sitting in the water and twisting around. (Fig. 98). He will have to use his hands in a pulling and pushing action to twist round.

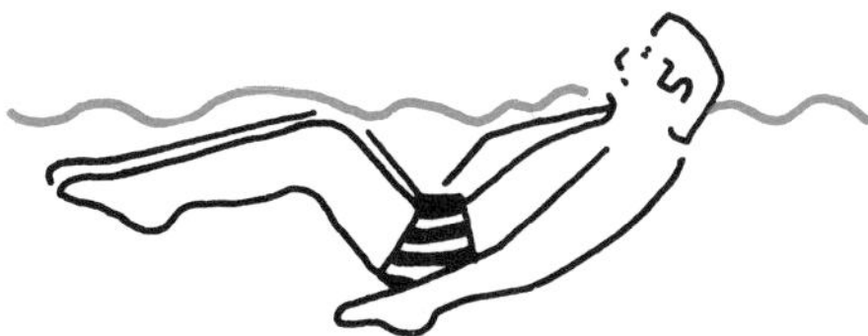

Fig. 98

3. Make him touch the end wall with one hand as he kicks into the wall (he will not use an arm stroke at this stage). He can then pivot round and push off.

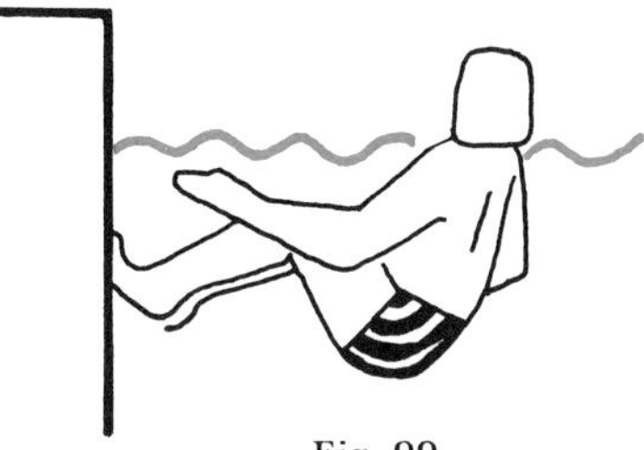

Fig. 99

4. Practise this type of turn–swimming back crawl into the wall.

Teaching out of the water pivot

1. Practise back somersaults in the water.

Fig. 100

2. Practise back somersaults with his head twisting a little to one side.

Fig. 101

3. From a standing position practise a half back somersault with a twist.
4. Practise a kicking approach using one arm extended over his head. (Fig. 102)
5. Practise full turn. (Fig. 103).

Fig. 102

Fig. 103

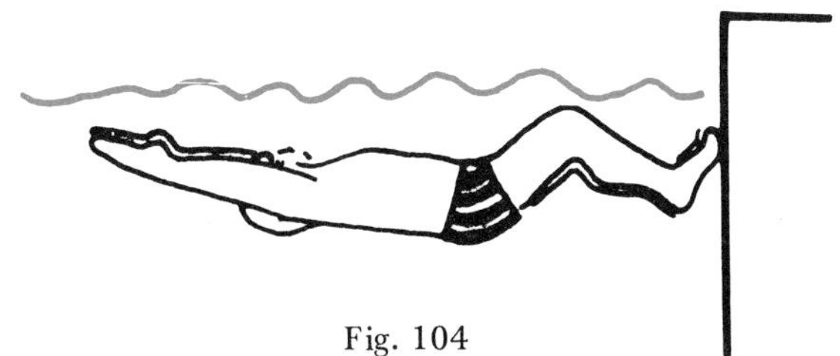

Fig. 104

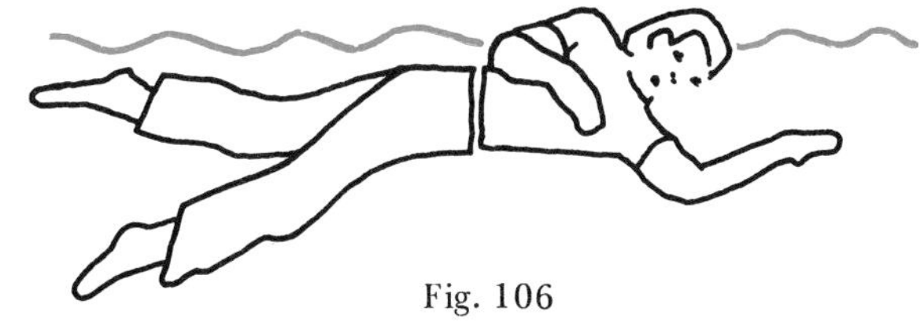

Fig. 106

OTHER WATER SKILLS

SURVIVAL SWIMMING

Swimming with clothes on—this is a necessary requisition for life-saving and survival skills.

The best strokes to practise in this particular case are Breast Stroke (Fig. 105), Side Stroke (Fig. 106) and Back Breast Stroke (Fig. 107). *DO NOT* rush the strokes— take your time.

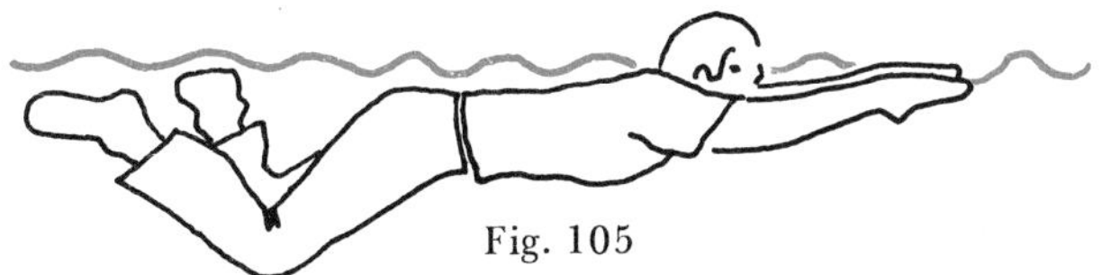

Fig. 105

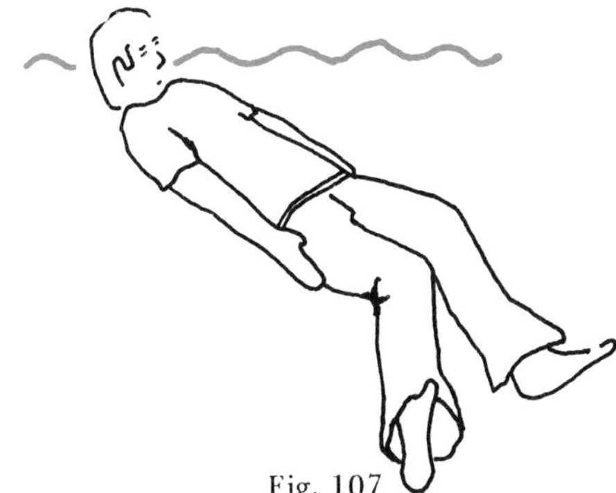

Fig. 107

Undressing in the water—requires a lot of practice. Do not rush your child. If necessary practice in depth of water where he can place both feet on the bottom. If he has to take anything over his head, then suggest that he rolls the clothes up in readiness (Fig. 108) so that they can be taken over his head in one action. It often helps if he goes under the water when undressing. (Fig. 109).

Fig. 108

Fig. 109

Using his clothes as floats.—This activity can sometimes be useful in an emergency. It is a great help when floating for long periods. The easiest way is to take your trousers off and force air into them.

First practise this skill in shallow water with feet on the bottom.

1. Tie knot in trouser leg (Fig. 110).

Take them behind and over the head (Fig. 111).

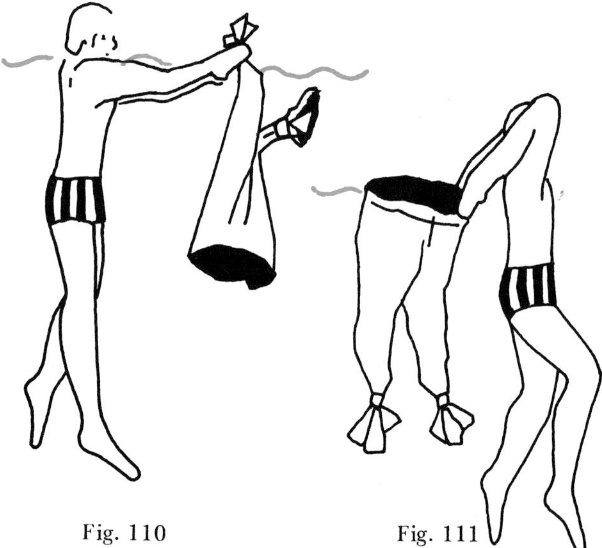

Fig. 110

Fig. 111

Fig. 112

Swing open end forcibly over his head and onto the surface of the water (Fig. 112).

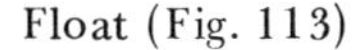

Float (Fig. 113)

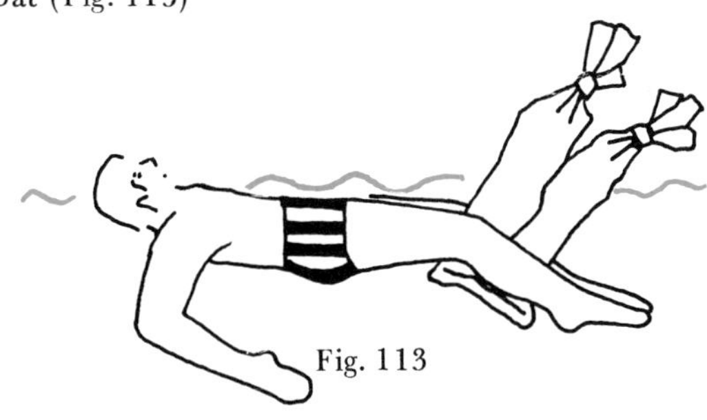

Fig. 113

Tread water

There are lots of different ways to do this.

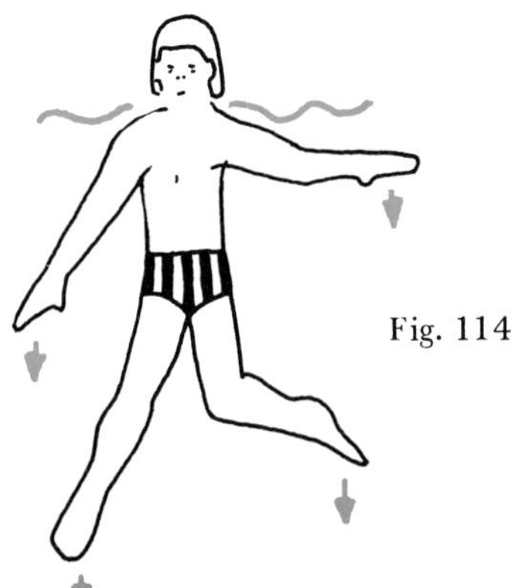

Fig. 114

Kick flat foot one leg at a time. Push arms down alternately (Fig. 114).

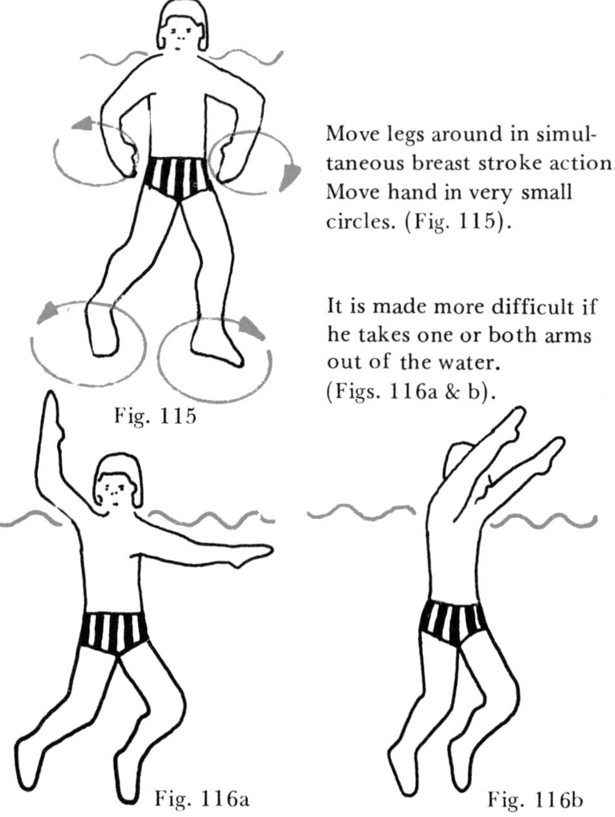

Fig. 115

Move legs around in simultaneous breast stroke action. Move hand in very small circles. (Fig. 115).

It is made more difficult if he takes one or both arms out of the water. (Figs. 116a & b).

Fig. 116a

Fig. 116b

Underwater swimming

He should swim breast stroke underwater similar to the start in competitive start (pages 73-74). Let him swim through hoop. (Fig. 117)

Fig. 117

SCULLING

Sculling can be fun and it is interesting how many different ways it can be done. The hand can be held flat on the water so that you remain stationary. (Fig. 118a).

Fig. 118a

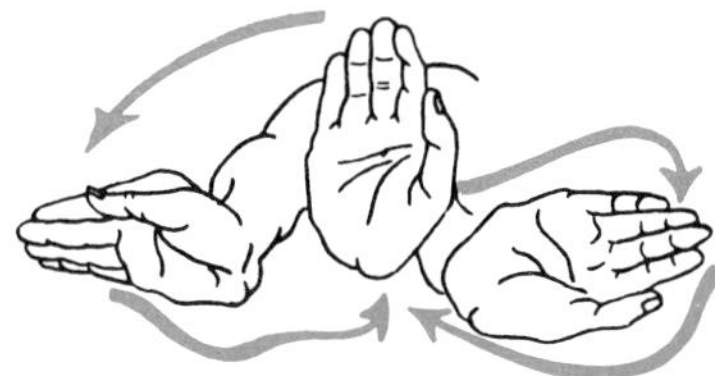

Fig. 118b

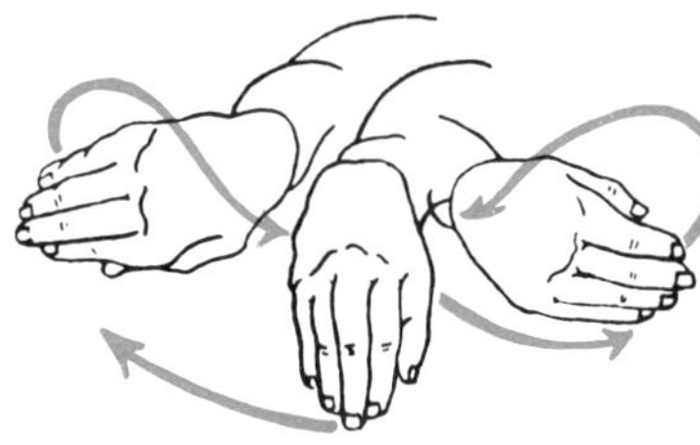

Fig. 118c

The hands can be raised towards the surface so that they push in the water which will make the body travel head first (Fig. 118b).

The hands can be lowered towards the bottom of the pool so that they can pull on the water making the body travel feet first.

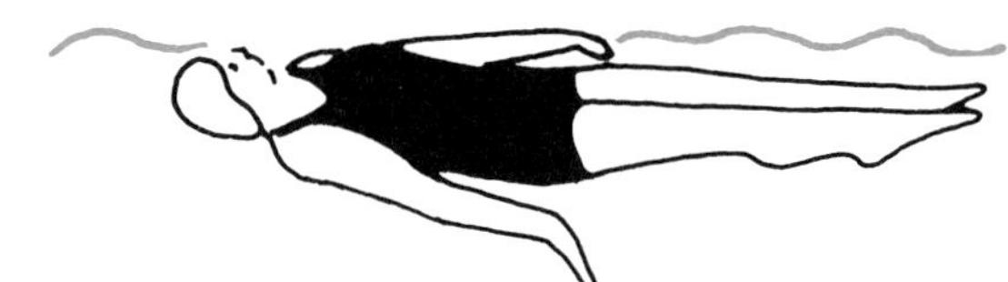

Fig. 119a

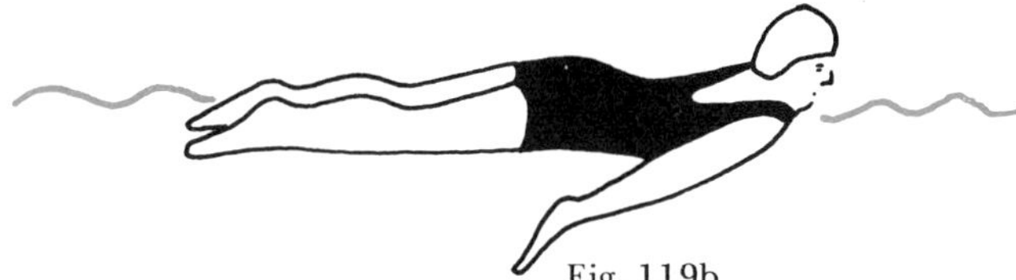

Fig. 119b

Normally travel head first.

Fig. 119c

Normal feet first.

Sculling can be done in many ways as well as directions. The hands can be held by the sides (Figs. 119a & b) or beyond the head (Fig. 119c).

If you get your child to practise different forms of sculling, many other movements of the body are possible, e.g. Sculling becomes increasingly difficult if one or both legs are raised out of the water (Fig. 120).

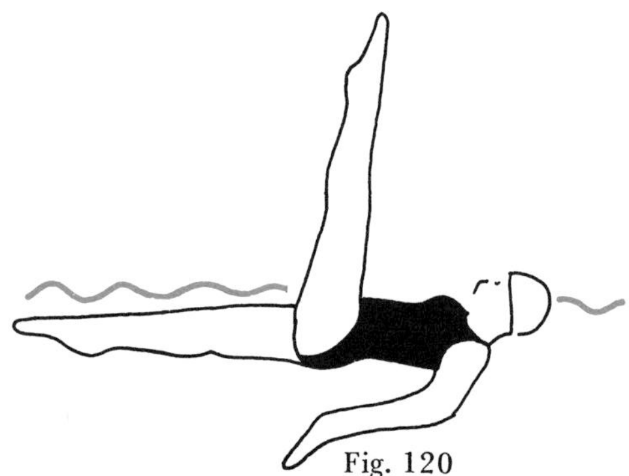

Fig. 120

Ballet leg single.

BALL SKILLS

Swimming with a ball. (Fig. 121)

Fig. 121

Picking up a ball and throwing it. (Fig. 122).
First press on the ball which will make it bob upwards. Allow the hand to slide underneath.

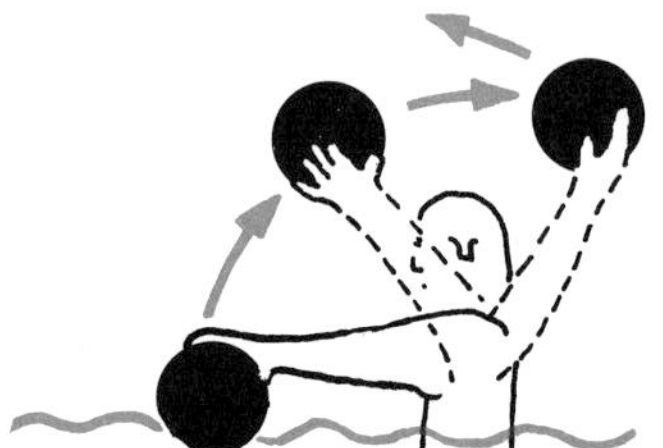

Fig. 122

Front somersault.
Tuck head in chest
and bend the knees.

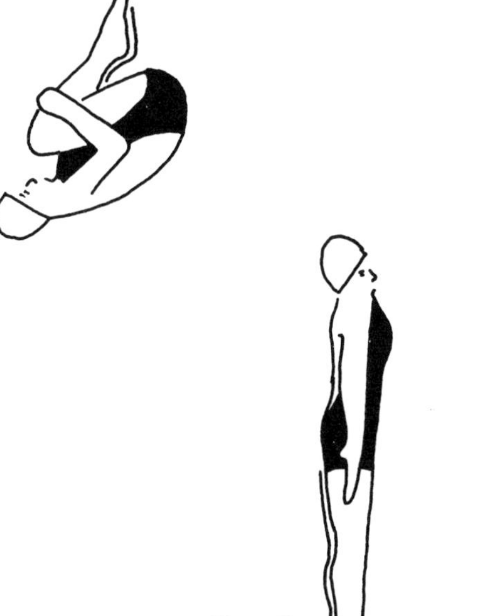

Fig. 123

Back dive.
Lean back and look for the water.

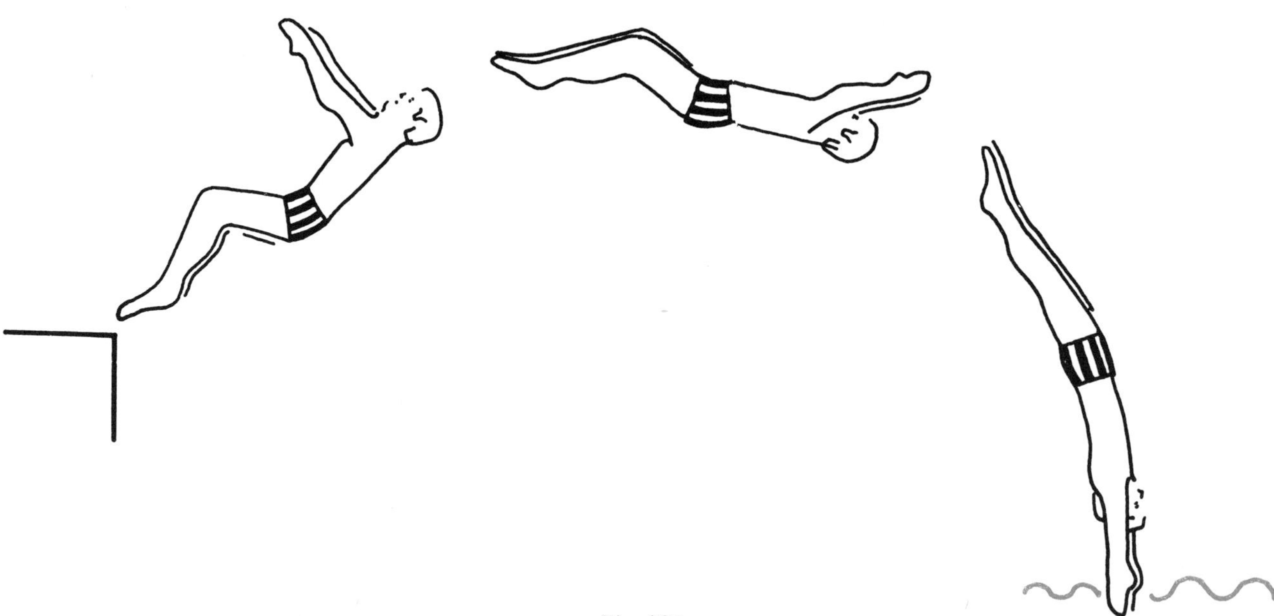

Fig. 124

Twisting dives.

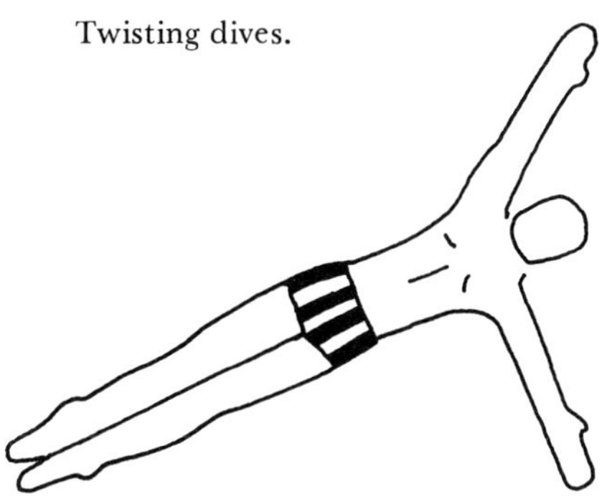

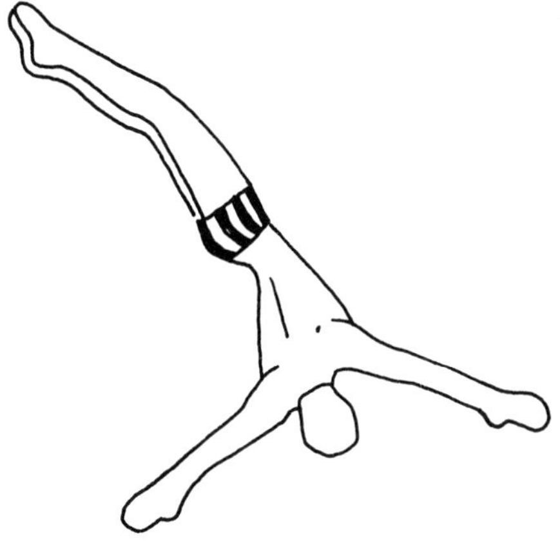

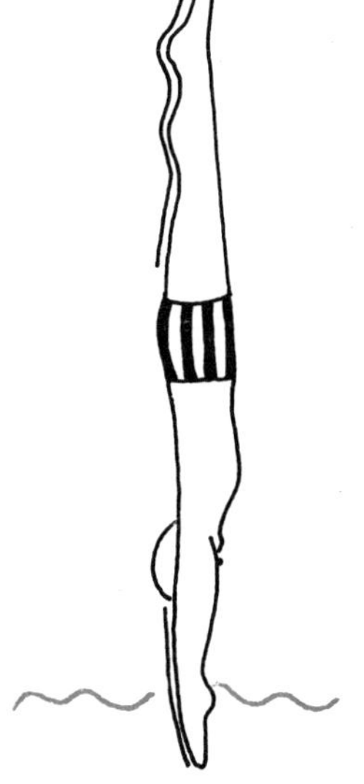

Fig. 125

Part 4
Awards

AWARDS HE CAN ACHIEVE

The Amateur Swimming Association, Harold Fern House, Derby Square, Loughborough, Leics, LE11 0AL, have the following awards:

Joint:

A.S.A. English Schools — Stage I and Stage II
A.S.A. Bronze Survival
A.S.A. Silver Survival
A.S.A. Gold Survival
A.S.A. Honours Survival

A typical award is SILVER

SILVER AWARD:
Dress as for men, boys trousers and shirt or long-legged pyjamas with the addition of a sleeveless or short-sleeved pullover.

1 Effect an entry from the side of the bath by a straddle or a tuck jump.
2 Swim 100 yards in less than 4 minutes.
3 Tread water for 1 minute in a vertical position, using legs and one arm only.
4 Tread water for 3 minutes in a vertical position.
5 Undress in the water and demonstrate the ability to make a float from clothing.
6 Surface dive in a depth of approximately 6 feet of water. (a) head first and (b) feet first and swim a minimum of 5 yards completely submerged, before re-surfacing on each occasion.
7 Swim 880 yards, of which 440 yards shall be on the back, and 440 yards on the front or side.
8 Climb out from deep water, as for Bronze Award.

A.S.A. Diving—typical award.

GRADE 2
From 4ft. firmboard or 1m. springboard into a minimum depth of 9 feet of water.

1 Plain Header.
2 Forward Dive, piked or tucked.
3 Inward Dive, piked or tucked.
4 Back Dive, piked, tucked or straight.

A.S.A. Synchronised
A.S.A. Water Polo Awards
A.S.A. Adult Swimming Awards

Other Associations have awards and their addresses are:

Royal Life Saving Society,
Desborough House,
14 Devonshire St.
Portland Place,
London W1N 2AT

Swimming Teacher Association,
1 Birmingham Rd.,
West Bromwich,
West Midlands,
B71 4JQ

'THE DOOR IS OPEN'

If you have been successful, and there is no reason why you should not be, you will have helped your child to 'open the door' onto a lifetime of healthy activity.

If he has the aptitude, he can join a Swimming Club which is affiliated to the Amateur Swimming Association.

As a member of one of these Clubs, he will be given more guidance and encouragement. He may even become good enough to compete for his country at an Olympic Games.

He may wish to follow other types of water sports, either as a recreation or for competition.

No matter what your child wishes to do in a water environment, you will have the satisfaction in knowing that you have been responsible for laying the right foundations.

GCSE
Biology for Double Science

David Applin

Hodder & Stoughton

A MEMBER OF THE HODDER HEADLINE GROUP

Using Mind Maps® in your revision

Mind Maps® can be a valuable aid to revision. They help you to organise your thoughts in a logical and easy-to-remember format. Sample Mind Maps® are provided on pages 50 and 76. Look at these. Try to use the model to help you revise other topics.

The "Teach Yourself" name and logo are registered trade marks of Hodder & Stoughton Ltd in the UK.

A catalogue record for this title is available from the British Library.

ISBN 0 340 74702 1

First published 1999
Impression number 10 9 8 7 6 5 4 3 2
Year 2000 1999

Editorial, design and production by Hart McLeod, Cambridge

Printed in Great Britain by Circle Services Ltd, Southend, Essex for Hodder & Stoughton Educational, a division of Hodder Headline Plc, 338 Euston Road, London NW1 3BH

Rapid Revision GCSE Biology for Double Science

Rapid Revision Planner

TOPIC 2 Cells

TOPIC 3 Plants as Organisms

TOPIC 4 Humans as Organisms

TOPIC 5 Inheritance and Evolution

Living Things and the Environment 1

Characteristics of life

The characteristics of life are the features that are common to all living things:

- **Movement** – animals move from place to place because of the action of muscles which pull on the **skeleton**; plants do not usually move from place to place – they move mainly by growing
- **Respiration** occurs in cells and releases energy from food for life's activities; **aerobic** respiration uses oxygen to release energy from food; **anaerobic** respiration releases energy from food without using oxygen
- **Sensitivity** allows living things to detect changes (**stimuli**) in their surroundings and take appropriate action (**response**)
- **Growth** leads to an increase in size
- **Reproduction** produces new individuals
- **Excretion** removes the waste substances produced by the chemical reactions (called **metabolism**) taking place in cells
- **Nutrition** makes food (by the process of **photosynthesis**) or takes in food for use in the body.

REMEMBERING the mnemonic **MRS GREN** will help you recall the characteristics of life.

Life on Earth

Why can planet Earth support life?
Because Earth is:

- close enough to the Sun for its surface temperature to be in the range in which life can exist (an average of 15°C)
- massive enough to have sufficient gravity to hold down an atmosphere of different gases essential for living organisms
- surrounded by a layer of ozone which stops too much ultraviolet light reaching the surface – excess ultraviolet light destroys living things.

Soil, air and **water** form Earth's environment.

Earth's physical environment

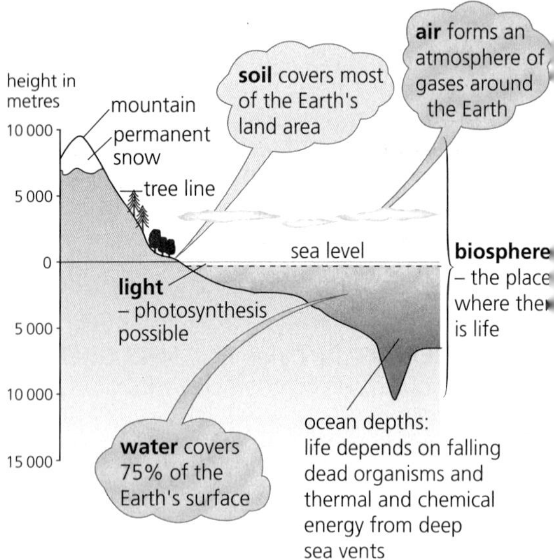

height in metres
10 000
5 000
0
5 000
10 000
15 000
mountain
permanent snow
tree line
soil covers most of the Earth's land area
air forms an atmosphere of gases around the Earth
sea level
biosphere – the place where the is life
light – photosynthesis possible
water covers 75% of the Earth's surface
ocean depths: life depends on falling dead organisms and thermal and chemical energy from deep sea vents

Classification

Organising living things into groups is called **classification**. Some characteristics are unique to the group, other characteristics are shared with other groups. Groups, therefore, combine to form larger groups. The largest group of all is the **kingdom**. Each:

- kingdom contains a number of **phyla**
- phyl**um** (singular) contains a number of **classes**
- class contains a number of **families**
- family contains a number of **genera**
- gen**us** (singular) contains one or more **species**.

The genus and the species identify the individual living thing. For example, humans belong to the genus *Homo* and have the species name *sapiens*. The method of naming living things in two parts is called the **binomial system**. There are **five kingdoms**:

- **Kingdom Plants** – organisms made of many cells – each cell is surrounded by a wall made of cellulose; food is produced by photosynthesis.
- **Kingdom Animals** – organisms made of many cells; food is taken in and usually digested inside the body.
- **Kingdom Fungi** – organisms made of many cells that form thread-like structures called hyphae.
- **Kingdom Protists** – single-celled organisms.
- **Kingdom Bacteria** – single-celled organisms – the cell body is simple in structure compared with protists.

Viruses are sub-microscopic particles – it is difficult to say if they are alive or not.

Identifying living things

A **key** is a means of identifying an unfamiliar organism from a selection of specimens. It consists of a set of descriptions. Each description is a clue that helps in the identification. A set of clues makes the key.

The easiest type of key to use is called a **dichotomous** key ('dichotomous' means branching into two). Each time the key branches, you have to choose between two statements. These may be presented diagrammatically as a chart, or written in pairs or **couplets**. By comparing the pairs of statements with the specimen, you will eventually find a description that fits. This identifies the organism. A key is therefore a route to a name. Different keys are used to name different living things. For example:

Identifying different fruits

1 Hairy skin? – GOOSEBERRY.
Non-hairy skin? – go to 2.

2 Pips on the fruit's surface? – STRAWBERRY.
No pips on the fruit's surface? – go to 3.

3 Nearly spherical in shape? – go to 4.
Other shape? – BANANA.

4 Smooth surface? – APPLE.
Rough surface? – go to 5.

5 Fruit made up of sub-units? – BLACKBERRY.
Fruit made up of one unit? – ORANGE.

What is an ecosystem?

Ecology involves studying relationships between organisms and between organisms and the environment. Organisms and environment together form an **ecosystem**. The organisms are the living – **biotic** – part of the ecosystem forming its **community**. The environment is the non-living – abiotic – part, consisting of air, soil and/or water. The relationship between the term ecosystem and other ecological terms is shown below.

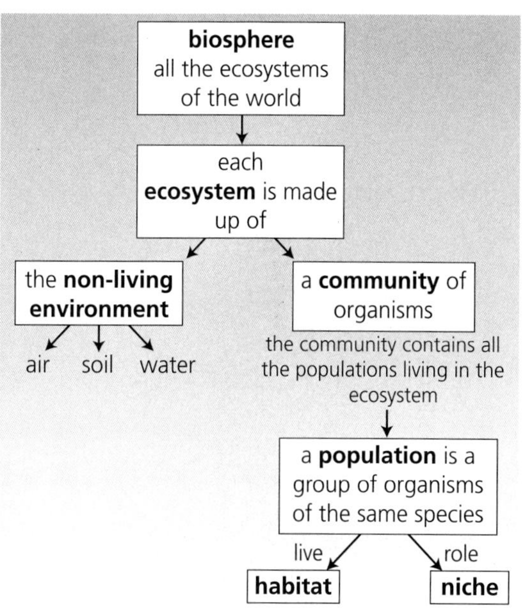

An oak wood ecosystem

Physical Environment

there may be up to 90% less light inside the wood than outside when the canopy is fully developed

THE ECOSYSTEM

HABITATS

canopy layer

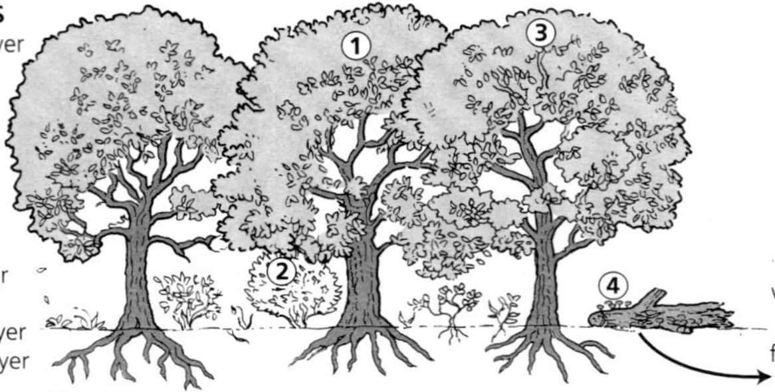

shrub layer
field layer
ground layer
detritus layer

COMMUNITY

1 oak tree
2 holly
3 pigeons, rooks living in canopy
4 toadstools on rotting log

EXAMPLE HABITAT

decomposers (which break down dead organic matter) at work on dead wood

Fungi and bacteria feed on the dead wood causing decomposition

NICHE: fungal hyphae decompose dead wood, releasing minerals into the environment

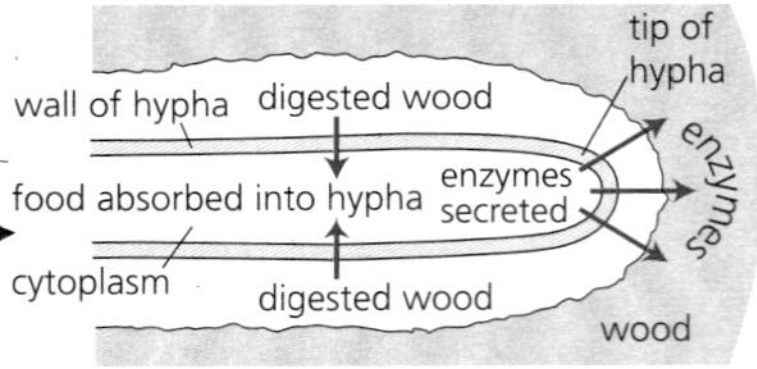

tip of hypha
wall of hypha
digested wood
enzymes
food absorbed into hypha
enzymes secreted
cytoplasm
digested wood
wood

Decomposition releases gases and minerals into the soil

Food chains

Plants, algae and some bacteria are called **producers** because they use sunlight to produce food by **photosynthesis**. Animals do not produce food. They are called **consumers** because they eat food.

- **Herbivores** eat plants.
- **Carnivores** eat meat.
- **Omnivores** eat both plants and meat.

Predators catch and eat other animals. **Prey** are the animals that are caught. **Scavengers** are carnivores that feed on dead bodies.

A **food chain** shows the links between plants, prey, predators and scavengers (see figure).

Food chain in an oak wood

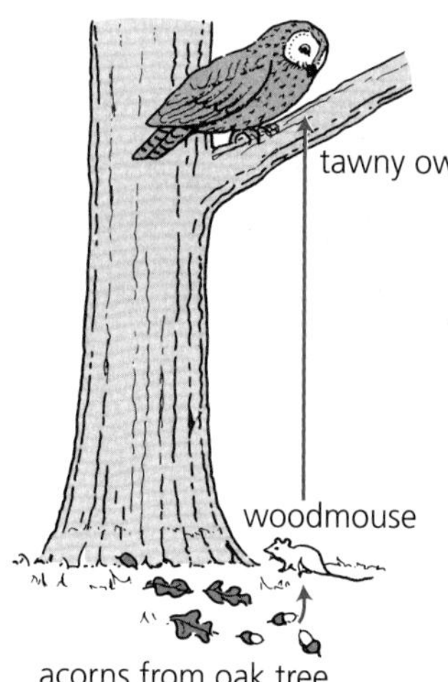

Notice that:

- the arrows represent the transfer of food between different organisms
- the arrows point from the eaten to the eater
- the number of links in a food chain is usually four or less.

Food webs

Most animals eat more than one type of plant or other animal. The feeding relationships are shown as a **food web** (see figure below). **Notice** that:

- several food chains link up to form a food web
- different types of animal may eat the same type of food.

A food web is usually a more accurate description of feeding relationships in a community than a food chain. Why? – Because a food web shows all the feeding links between plants, prey, predators and scavengers.

Food web in an oak wood

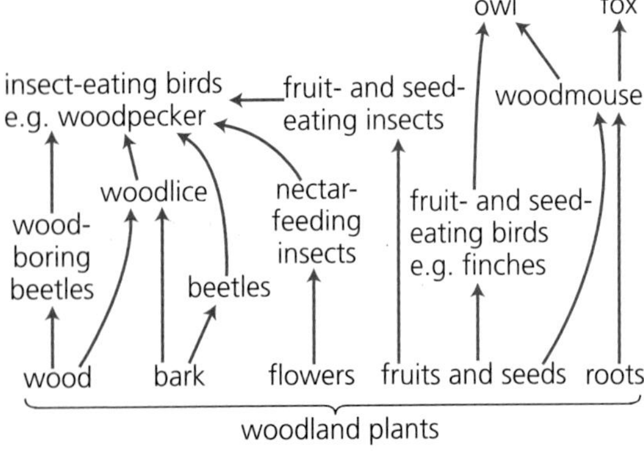

REMEMBER that food chains and food webs begin with producers. Why? – Because producers can use sunlight to produce food by photosynthesis.

Ecological pyramids

REMEMBER that many plants support a limited number of herbivores which in turn support fewer carnivores. Food chains and food webs do not tell us about the number of individuals involved. **Ecological pyramids** do!

Pyramid of numbers for a grassland community in 0.1 hectare

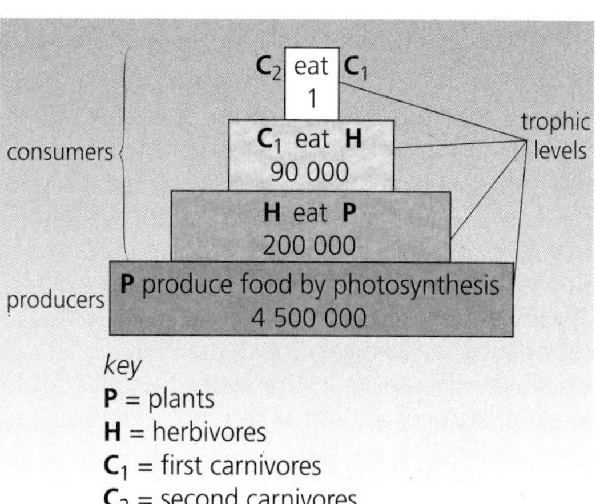

Notice that the **pyramid of numbers** for a grassland community has several feeding levels called **trophic levels** (all ecological pyramids are built of trophic levels).

Each trophic level groups together organisms that have similar types of food. Pyramids of numbers show the numbers of organisms in each trophic level.

Ecological pyramids for a woodland community

Pyramid of numbers for a woodland community

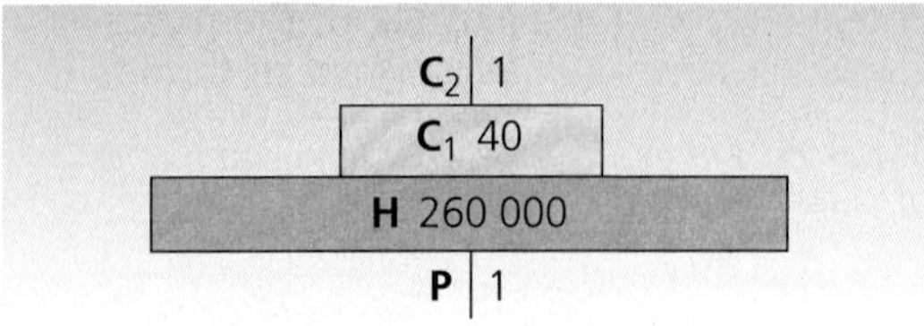

Notice that the pyramid of numbers for a woodland community has a point at the bottom as well as the top. Why? – Because relatively few producers (trees) support a large number of herbivores and carnivores. Why? – Because trees are large! A numbers pyramid for a woodland does not accurately describe woodland feeding relationships. Why? – Because differences in the **size** of producers and consumers are not taken into account.

Pyramid of biomass for a woodland community

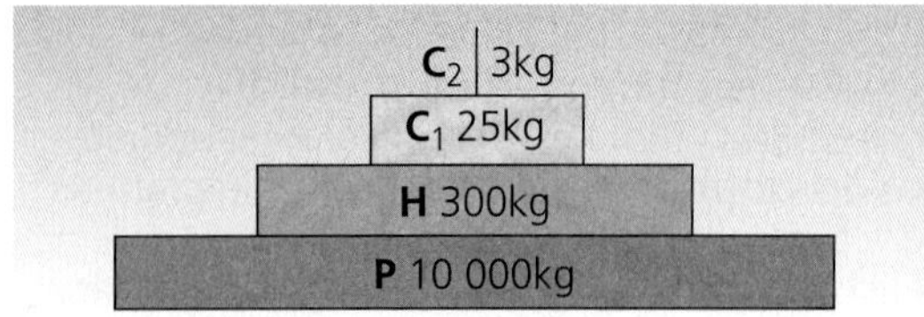

A **pyramid of biomass** allows for differences in the size of organisms. Why? – Because the pyramid shows the **amount of organic material** (as dry mass) in each trophic level.

Pyramid of energy

A **pyramid of energy** shows energy flow through, and energy loss from, a community in a given time. Its shape therefore is not affected by differences in size.

Pyramid of energy for a stream (in kJ/m²/year)

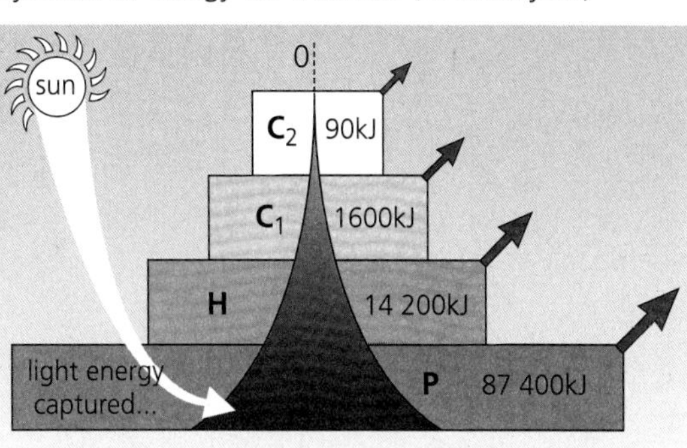

key energy lost from each trophic level through life's activities

flow of food energy through the community from one trophic level to the next (feeding)

Notice that:

- feeding transfers food energy from one trophic level to the next
- energy is lost from each trophic level – mostly as heat released by the metabolism of cells

★ as a result the amount of food energy in a trophic level is less than the one below it
★ as a result the amount of living material (biomass) in a trophic level is less than the one below it.

Now you know why there is a limited number of links in a food chain (see page 13).

See also • p.7 **Metabolism**

Decomposition and the nitrogen cycle

Decomposition releases **mineral nutrients** into the soil. The nutrients are essential for the growth of plants and animals. They circulate between the environment and organisms. The **nitrogen cycle** is an example.

Nitrogen circulates from air to soil to living things and back again in the nitrogen cycle

nitrogen in the air

lightning, engines and furnaces combine nitrogen and oxygen forming nitrogen oxides and nitric acid which falls as **acid rain**

fertilizers containing ammonium salts and nitrates replace the nutrients which are taken from the soil when crops are harvested

some nitrates and ammonium salts are converted into gaseous nitrogen by **denitrifying** bacteria

animals are unable to synthesise certain amino acids: they must eat plants or other animals to obtain them

protein in plants

protein in animals

plants take in nitrates through their roots and synthesise proteins

ammonium salts enter the soil in the excreta of animals and decaying plant and animal remains

nitrogen-fixing bacteria in the root nodules of beans, peas, etc., turn nitrogen into nitrates which plants absorb in solution

nitrates in the soil

nitrifying bacteria in the soil convert ammonium salts into nitrates which plants can absorb

ammonium salts in the soil

 See also • p.12 **Decomposition**

Decomposition and the carbon cycle

The carbon cycle shows those processes that put carbon dioxide into the air and those that remove carbon dioxide from the air

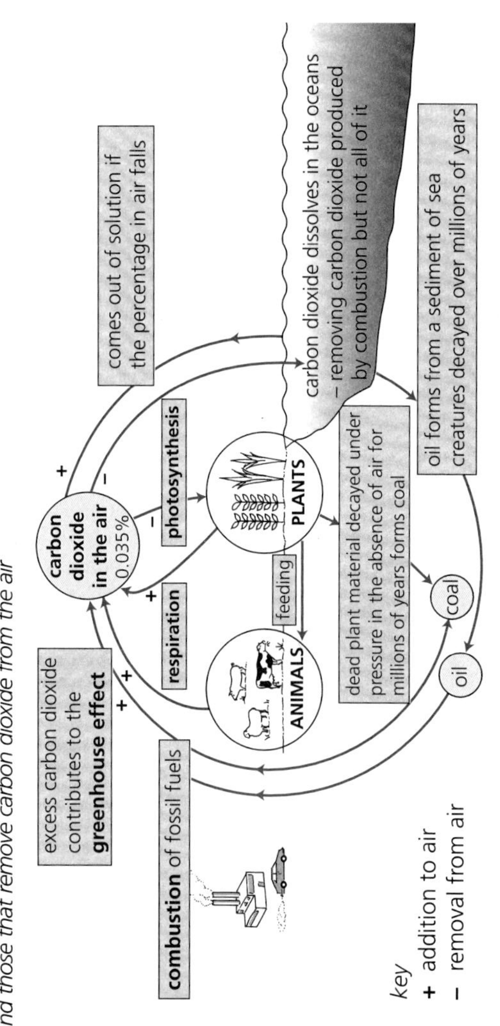

carbon dioxide in the air 0.035%
comes out of solution if the percentage in air falls
carbon dioxide dissolves in the oceans – removing carbon dioxide produced by combustion but not all of it
photosynthesis
PLANTS
respiration
feeding
ANIMALS
dead plant material decayed under pressure in the absence of air for millions of years forms coal
oil forms from a sediment of sea creatures decayed over millions of years
coal
oil
excess carbon dioxide contributes to the greenhouse effect
combustion of fossil fuels
key
+ addition to air
– removal from air

See also • p.39 **Photosynthesis** • p.59 **Respiration** • p.24 **Greenhouse effect**

Distribution of organisms

Different factors affect the **distribution** of organisms. Physical factors include: • the amount of light • the abundance of water. Biological factors include: • **intraspecific competition** – competition between individuals of the same species • **interspecific competition** – competition between individuals of different species • **adaptations** of organisms for survival in different environments • **interactions** between predators and prey.

Predators are adapted to catch prey, and prey are adapted to escape predators:

Predator	Prey
Catches a variety of species, reducing the risk of starvation should one prey decline in numbers Catches young, old and sick prey Catches large prey which provide more food per kill Moves to areas where prey is plentiful Camouflage allows predator to 'surprise' prey	Large groups (e.g. herds), distract predators from concentrating on a particular individual Stings and bitter tastes deter predators Warning coloration tells predators to avoid particular prey Shock tactics startle predators Camouflage conceals prey Prey tries to run/swim/fly faster than predator

REMEMBER that rivals for something in short supply (e.g. water, light, space) are competitors. **REMEMBER** that organisms are **adapted** (suited) for the environment in which they live and for their role (niche) in that environment.

 See also • p.11 **Niche** • p.13 **Predator** • p.9 **Species** • p.13 **Prey** • p.94 **Evolution**

Population size

Limiting factors in the growth of populations include, **shortages of** food, oxygen, water, light and shelter **and build up of** poisonous wastes, predators, parasites, disease and social factors.

Population growth curve

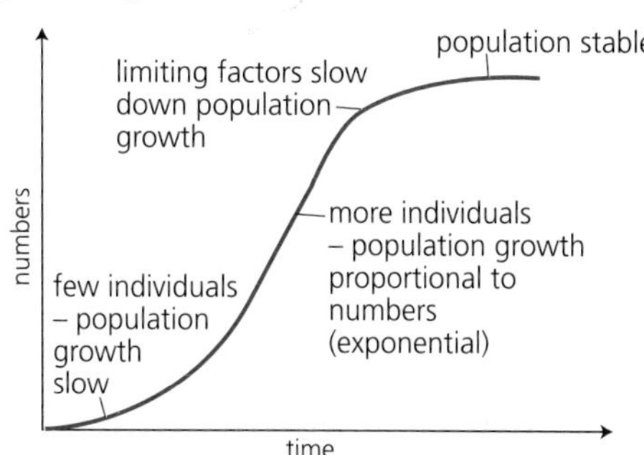

Predator – prey relationships

A predator and its prey affect the size of the other's population.

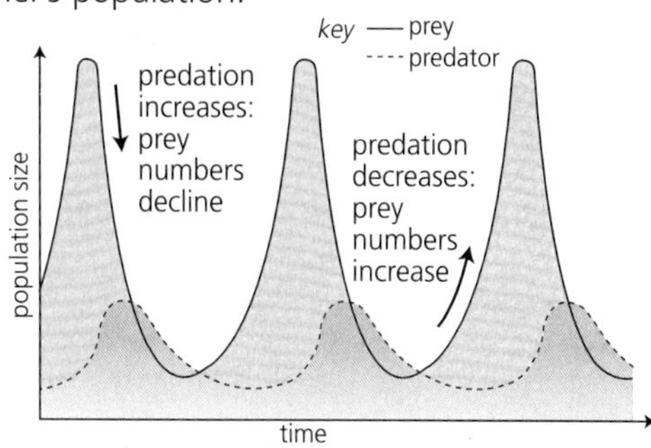

Improvements in food production, medical care and public health have led to an **increase** in the human population. Better contraception, economic development and the changing role of women **all** help to **slow** growth.

See also • p.11 **Population**

Producing food

The amount of food a farm produces depends on:

- the amount of energy entering the farm ecosystem
- the efficiency with which the energy is converted into plant and animal tissue.

REMEMBER that the **fewer** the links in a food chain, the **less** food energy is lost and so the **more** food is available to consumers. Energy transfer between producers and consumers is inefficient because:

- undigested plant material passes out of the herbivore body as faeces
- the herbivore uses energy to stay alive.

Therefore eating meat is wasteful in terms of food energy.

Intensive farming

Intensive farming methods are used to produce as much food as possible from the land available:

- **monoculture** – where a single crop is grown over a large area
- **artificial fertilisers** supply nutrients directly to crops
- **irrigation** brings water to land that would otherwise be too dry to grow crops
- **mechanisation** – farm machinery works best in large, open fields – fuel oil powers the machinery
- use of **pesticides**: **insecticides** kill insects, **herbicides** kill weeds, **fungicides** kill fungi.

 See also • p.13 **Food chains** • p.17 **Pyramid of energy**
• p.43 **Plant nutrients**

Pollution

Pollution is caused by **industry** making goods that maintain our standard of living and **intensive farming** that produces large quantities of food. **Acid rain** (pH 2.4–5.0) results from industrial processes releasing gases which react with water vapour and oxygen in the air:

- **sulphur dioxide** forms sulphuric acid (H_2SO_4)
- **oxides of nitrogen** form nitric acid (HNO_3)

★ as a result mineral salts (nutrients) needed for healthy plant growth are removed – **leached** – from the soil

★ as a result acid rain enters rivers and lakes killing wildlife.

Using low-sulphur fuels and removing sulphur dioxide from the waste gases leaving chimneys helps to reduce the amount of sulphur dioxide entering the atmosphere. The **ozone layer** – 5km thick – surrounds the Earth at a distance of 25–30 km from the Earth's surface. It cuts out some of the Sun's ultraviolet light which would otherwise be harmful to life but there are gaps in the layer now. Ozone oxidises pollutants that accumulate in the upper atmosphere.

- **Chlorofluorohydrocarbons** (CFCs) which are aerosol **propellants** react with ozone producing oxygen.
- **Nitrogen monoxide** coming from the exhausts of high altitude aircraft reacts with oxygen to form nitrogen dioxide.

The use of CFCs is being reduced.

See also • p.39 **Photosynthesis** • p.60 **Haemoglobin** • p.13 **Food chains**

Pollution – continued

Carbon dioxide and water vapour in the atmosphere warm the Earth's surface naturally – the **greenhouse effect**. However the Earth's surface has warmed up by 0.75°C during the last one hundred years. Why?

- Burning **fossil fuels** releases carbon dioxide into the air.
- **Clear felling** tropical rain forests reduces the amount of vegetation taking carbon dioxide from the air for **photosynthesis**.
- Increasing rice cultivation and numbers of livestock releases large volumes of **methane** (another greenhouse gas) into the air.

Warming of the Earth's surface will probably increase the rate of **melting** of the polar ice caps:

★ as a result sea levels will rise
★ as a result coastal areas will be flooded.

Nitrate fertilisers – excess contaminates water:

- fertilisation of the water increases the rate of growth of algae; when the algae die, bacteria decompose the dead material using up available oxygen (increasing **Biological Oxygen Demand**), so killing wildlife
- nitrates are converted into **nitrites** – which the body converts into **nitrosamines** a cause of cancer; **also** in babies nitrites reduce the ability of haemoglobin to combine with oxygen.

Pesticides kill wildlife, some insecticides (e.g. DDT, dieldrin) persist in the environment, **accumulate** in food chains and may cause illness in humans. In USA and Europe, DDT is now **banned**.

Living Things and the Environment

Questions

1 List the different components of an ecosystem.
2 Briefly describe how a biological key is used.
3 In the 1890s, when people saw cars for the first time, many thought that the cars were alive. Imagine that you are a reporter writing a short article for the local newspaper reassuring the populace that although cars seemed to move under their own steam, they were not alive.
4 (a) Why is a food web a more accurate description of feeding in a community than a food chain?
(b) Why do food chains and food webs always begin with plants?
5 Give reasons for the rapid increase in human population.

Answers

1 physical or abiotic environment / living or biotic community / habitats / niches **2** the unfamiliar specimen is compared against the descriptions in the key until the description that matches the specimen is found; this identifies the specimen **3** although cars move; need fuel (= nutrition); burn fuel (= respiration); and produce waste gases (= excretion); they do not grow or reproduce and are not sensitive. Cars therefore do not show all the characteristics associated with living things **4** (a) most animals eat more than one type of plant or other animal / a food web shows the range of different food eaten (b) plants produce food by photosynthesis / animals consume this food directly when they eat plants or indirectly when they eat other animals which depend on plant food
5 improvements in food production; more jobs; new drugs (accept improvement in medicines/medical care); improvement in public health

Cell structure

Microscopes help us see cells

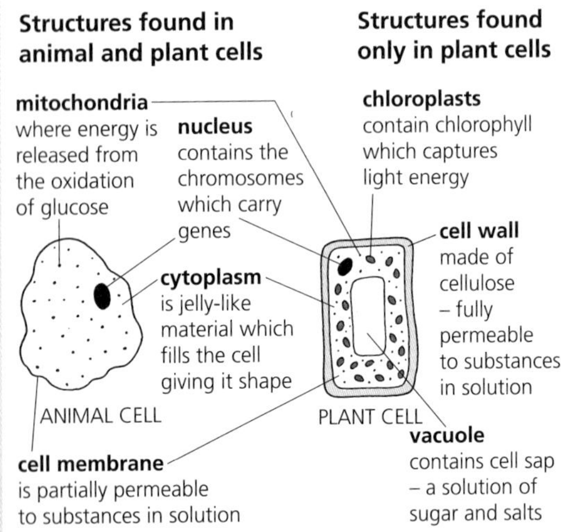
Structures found in animal and plant cells
Structures found only in plant cells
mitochondria where energy is released from the oxidation of glucose
nucleus contains the chromosomes which carry genes
chloroplasts contain chlorophyll which captures light energy
cell wall made of cellulose – fully permeable to substances in solution
cytoplasm is jelly-like material which fills the cell giving it shape
ANIMAL CELL
PLANT CELL
vacuole contains cell sap – a solution of sugar and salts
cell membrane is partially permeable to substances in solution

More than 200 different types of cell make up the human body. Fewer types of cell make up the plant body. Each type of cell is suited (**adapted**) for its particular **function** (the way it works). For example:

- **sperm cells** each have a tail-like flagellum that helps the sperm swim to an egg
- **red blood cells** transport oxygen around the body
- **leaf palisade cells** each contain chloroplasts packed with chlorophyll which absorbs light.

Molecules on the move

Substances move inside, and into and out of cells (see figure on page 28).

Diffusion: the movement of a substance through a solution or gas **down** a **concentration gradient** (that is, from a region of high concentration to a region of low concentration). The steeper the concentration gradient, the faster the substance diffuses.

Active transport: the movement of a substance through a solution **up** (against) a concentration gradient (that is, from a region of low concentration to a region of high concentration).

- Cells may build up **stores** of a substance which would otherwise be spread out by diffusion.
- Active transport requires more energy than diffusion.

Osmosis: the movement of **water down** a concentration gradient through a **partially permeable** membrane. A partially permeable membrane allows some substances to pass through but stops others. The passage of substances across such a membrane depends on the:

- size of the molecules
- size of the membrane pores
- surface area of the membrane
- rate of diffusion.

Diffusion, active transport and osmosis

Diffusion

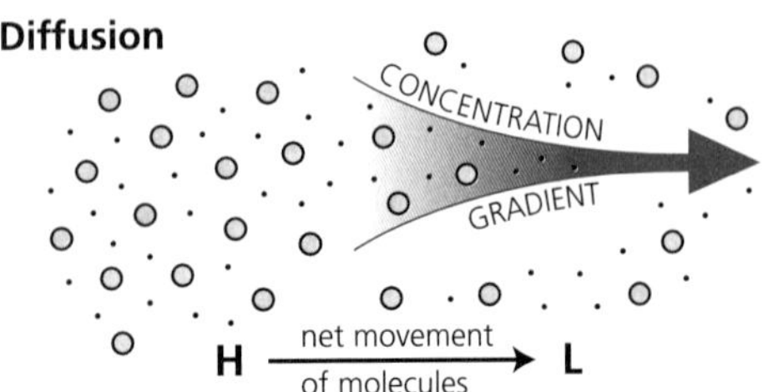

Active transport

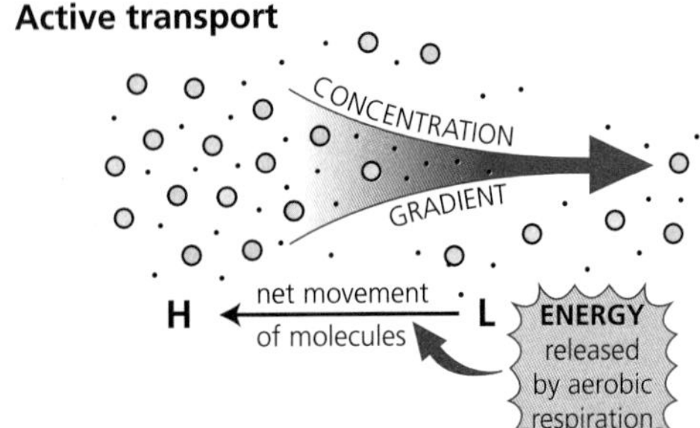

Osmosis

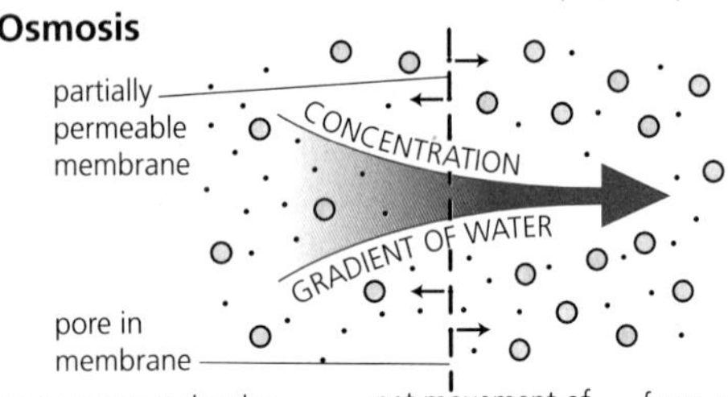

more water molecules on this side of membrane so more water molecules pass from left to right

net movement of water molecules

fewer water molecules on this side of membrane so fewer water molecules pass from right to le

key

O molecules of substance

• water molecules

H high concentration of substances in solution

L low concentration of substances in solution

Cells, tissues and organs

Plants and animals are made of many types of cells – they are **multicellular**.

- A group of similar cells makes a **tissue**.
- Different tissues together make up an **organ**.
- Different organs combine to make an **organ system**.

Surface area to volume ratio

All cells **exchange** materials with their environment. **REMEMBER** that as a cell grows its:

- surface area (SA) increases with the square (power^2) of the side
- volume (V) increases with the cube (power^3) of the side

★as a result, the larger the cell becomes, the smaller its surface area to volume ratio (SA/V)

- after a cell reaches a certain size its surface area becomes too small to meet the needs of the larger volume of living matter inside
- at this point the cell divides into two smaller daughter cells, each with a larger SA/V than the parent cell

★as a result the cells can exchange sufficient material between themselves and the environment.

Different organs and organ systems are specialised to make the SA/V as large as possible:

- **villi** increase the SA of the gut wall for the absorption of food
- **alveoli** increase the SA of the lungs for the diffusion of gases
- **root branches** and **root hairs** increase the SA for the absorption of water.

See also • p.53 **Villi** • p.57 **Alveoli** • p.42 **Roots**

Cell division

Cells divide in one of two ways (see figures page 31 and page 32):

Mitosis produces new (**daughter**) cells with the same number of chromosomes as the parent cell. The daughter cells are described as **diploid** (or **2n**). The **cells of the body** – except the cells of the sex organs which give rise to the sex cells (**gametes**) – divide by mitosis.

Meiosis produces daughter cells each with only half the number of chromosomes of the parent cell. The daughter cells are described as **haploid** (or **n**). **Sex cells** (sperms and eggs) are produced by meiosis.

The importance of mitosis

The daughter cells each receive an identical **full** (diploid) set of chromosomes from the parent cell. As a result:

★ the parent cell and its daughter cells are genetically identical – they form a **clone**
★ mitosis is the way in which living things repair damage; grow; reproduce asexually.

The importance of meiosis

The daughter cells each receive a **half** (haploid) set of chromosomes from the parent cell. As a result:

★ during fertilisation the chromosomes from the sperm and egg combine
★ the fertilised egg – **zygote** – is diploid but inherits a new combination of genes contributed (50:50) from the parents
★ the new individual inherits characteristics from both parents.

 See also • p.82 **Sex cells** • p.82 **Reproduction**

Mitosis and meiosis – sequence of events

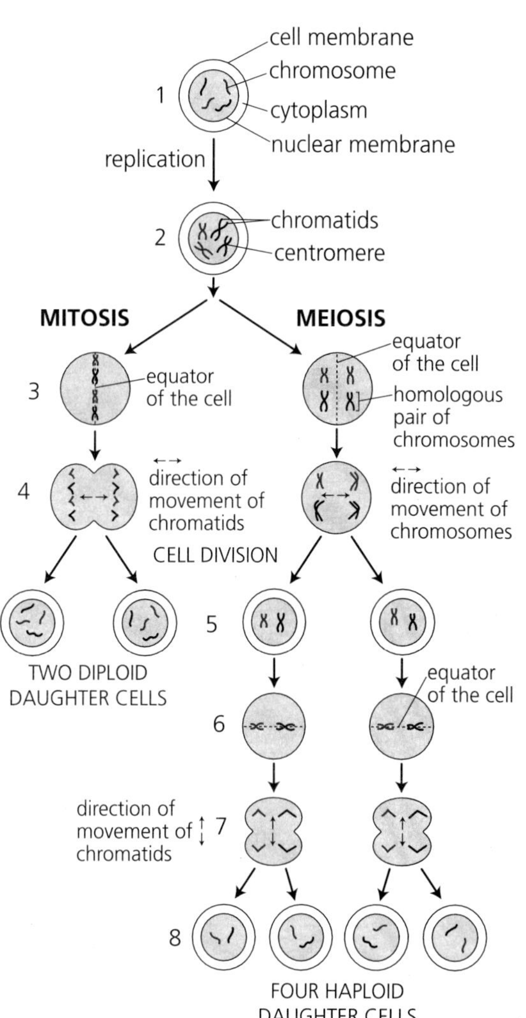

Comparing mitosis and meiosis

Mitosis	Meiosis
1 The chromosomes shorten, fatten and become visible under a microscope	1 The chromosomes shorten, fatten and become visible under a microscope
2 Each chromosome divides into a pair of identical (replica) **chromatids** joined to one another by the **centromere**	2 Each chromosome divides into a pair of identical (replica) **chromatids** joined to one another by the **centromere**
3 The chromatids line up on the equator (middle) of the cell – the nuclear membrane has disappeared	3 Matching chromosomes form **homologous** pairs and line up on the equator (middle) of the cell – the nuclear membrane disappears
4 The chromatids separate and move to the opposite ends of the cell, which begins to divide	4 Homologous pairs of chromosomes separate
5 The chromatids are now the new chromosomes of the two daughter cells – a nuclear membrane forms around each group of chromosomes.	5 A new nuclear membrane forms around each group of chromosomes – the cell divides
	6 The nuclear membrane disappears – the chromosomes (still as pairs of chromatids) arrange themselves on the equator (middle) of the cell
	7 The chromatids separate, they are now the new chromosomes – each cell begins to divide
	8 Cell division occurs and a nuclear membrane forms around each group of chromosomes.

 See also • p 30 **Cell division** • p. 31 **Mitosis and meiosis**

Chemicals in living things – carbohydrates

The mnemonic **CHNOPS** helps you remember important elements in order of their abundance in living matter.

- carbon (C)
- hydrogen (H)
- nitrogen (N)
- oxygen (O)
- phosphorus (P)
- sulphur (S)

Carbohydrates contain carbon, hydrogen and oxygen. They are a source of energy and structural materials. There are three categories: **Monosaccharides** are simple sugars. Sweet-tasting **fructose** and **glucose** are examples – both have the molecular formula $C_6H_{12}O_6$ but different structural formulas. **Disaccharides** are complex sugars. They are formed when two monosaccharides combine. For example:

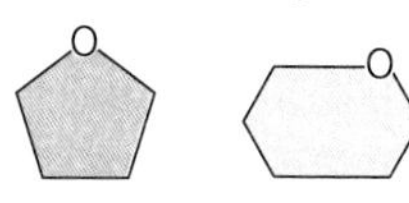

fructose glucose

maltose

$$2 \text{ glucose} \rightarrow \text{maltose} + \text{water}$$
$$2\,C_6H_{12}O_6 \rightarrow C_{12}H_{22}O_{11}\,(aq) + H_2O$$

Polysaccharides are formed from hundreds of sugar rings joined together:

- **starch** is a food substance stored in plants
- **glycogen** is a food substance stored in animals
- **cellulose** is a component of the cell walls of plants
- **chitin** is a component of the exoskeleton of insects.

Lipids and proteins

Lipids contain carbon, hydrogen and oxygen. Fats are solid at room temperature and oils are liquid at room temperature.

A **triglyceride** forms as follows:

glycerol + fatty acid → triglyceride + water

$$\begin{array}{l}-OH\\-OH\\-OH\end{array} + 3HA \longrightarrow \begin{array}{l}-A\\-A\\-A\end{array} + 3H_20$$

Lipids are a mixture of triglycerides.

Saturated fats form from fatty acids in which the carbon atoms are joined by **single** bonds. **Unsaturated** fats form from fatty acids in which the carbon atoms have **double** bonds between them. Fats and oils are important as:

- components of cell membranes
- sources of energy
- sources of fat-soluble vitamins A, D and E
- insulation which helps keep the body warm
- protection for delicate organs.

Proteins contain carbon, hydrogen, oxygen, nitrogen and sometimes sulphur.
Amino acids combine to make **peptides** and proteins – there are about 20 different amino acids.

Proteins are the materials from which new tissues are made during **growth** and **repair**.

- **Enzymes** are proteins which control the rates of chemical reactions in cells – **metabolism**.
- **Hormones** are proteins which control the activities of organisms.

Nucleic acids

Lengths of **deoxyribonucleic acid (DNA)** form the **genes** that carry information from parents to offspring. They carry the **genetic code** which tells cells how to assemble amino acids in the correct order to make proteins. **Ribonucleic acid (RNA)** transfers the information in genes to the places in the cell where proteins are made. DNA and RNA are made from smaller molecules called **nucleotides**.

- Each nucleotide consists of sugar – deoxyribose in DNA; ribose in RNA; phosphate and a base – one of either **adenine** (A), **cytosine** (C), **guanine** (G) or **thymine** (T); in RNA **uracil** (U) replaces (T).
- Many nucleotides join together to form a strand of DNA (or RNA).
- When two strands link together by **base pairing** (always A pairs with T and G pairs with C) and twist into a spiral, a **double helix** forms.

The double helix: two spiral strands connected by their bases

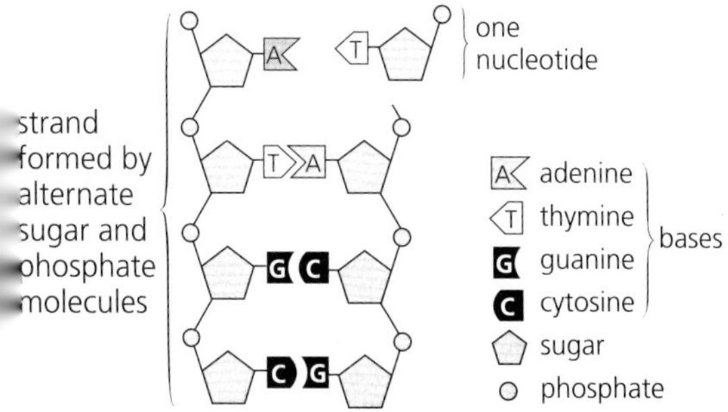

one nucleotide
strand formed by alternate sugar and phosphate molecules
A T
T A
G C
C G
A adenine
T thymine
G guanine
C cytosine
bases
sugar
phosphate

Enzymes in action

Enzymes are proteins made by living cells. They are catalysts which control the speed of chemical reactions in cells. Enzymes are:

- **specific** in their action – each enzyme catalyses a certain chemical reaction or type of chemical reaction
- sensitive to changes in **pH**
- sensitive to changes in **temperature**.

The substance that the enzyme helps to react is called the **substrate**. The substances formed in the reaction are called **products**. The features of enzymes are shown on page 37. Enzymes also speed up the **digestion** of food in the **gut**. They catalyse the breakdown of food by **hydrolysis**. Water splits large molecules of food into smaller molecules which are suitable for **absorption** into the body. Enzymes are useful **industrial catalysts**.

- Only a particular reaction is catalysed by an enzyme, making it easier to collect and purify the products.
- Enzyme activity is high at moderate temperature and pH.
- Only small amounts of enzyme are required.
- The enzyme is not used up in the reaction.

Enzymes bonded to insoluble supporting materials, **immobilised enzymes**, are:

- easily recovered to re-use
- active at temperatures that would destroy unprotected enzymes
- not diluted and therefore do not contaminate the product.

 See also • **Rapid Revision Chemistry, Topic 2,** p. 82
• p.53 **Absorption** • p.54 **Digestive enzymes**

Enzymes – continued

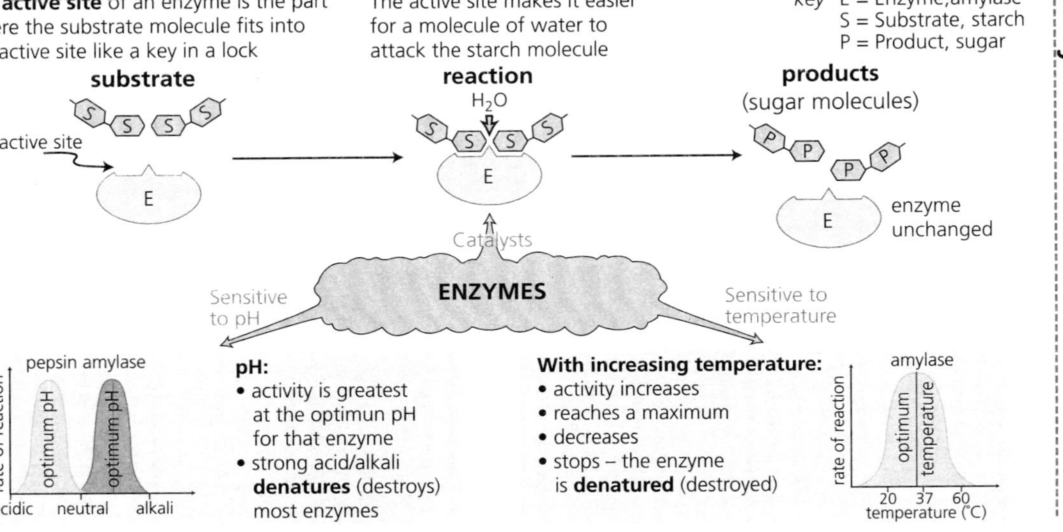

pH:

- activity is greatest at the optimun pH for that enzyme
- strong acid/alkali **denatures** (destroys) most enzymes

With increasing temperature:

- activity increases
- reaches a maximum
- decreases
- stops – the enzyme is **denatured** (destroyed)

Cells

Questions

1 Which of the structures listed below are found in (a) animal cells and plant cells (b) plant cells only? **nucleus cell membrane cell wall large vacuole mitochondria chloroplasts cytoplasm**

2 Describe what happens in the cells of a plant deprived of water which is then watered.

3 Compare and contrast the processes of mitosis and meiosis by listing the similarities and the differences.

4 Match each substance in column A with its function in column B.

A	B
Fat	Carries the genetic code
Cellulose	Insulates the body
DNA	A food substance stored in the liver
Glycogen	A component of the plant cell wall

Answers

1

Animal cells and plant cells		**Plant cells only**
nucleus	mitochondria	cell wall chloroplasts
cell membrane	cytoplasm	large vacuole

2 water is taken into the cells by osmosis / the cells become turgid **3 similarities** – replication of each chromosome into chromatids / lining up of the chromosomes on the equator of the cell / separation of the chromatids / chromatids are the new chromosomes in daughter cells / destruction and reformation of the nuclear membrane during the process of cell division **differences** – chromosomes form homologous pairs in meiosis but not mitosis / there are two divisions during meiosis but only one division during mitosis / meiosis results in four daughter cells; mitosis results in two daughter cells

4

A	B
fat	insulates the body
cellulose	a component of the plant cell wall
DNA	carries the genetic code
glycogen	a food substance stored in the liver

Photosynthesis

Chlorophyll is a green pigment which traps the energy of **sunlight**. The energy powers the chemical reactions of **photosynthesis** inside the **chloroplasts** of the **leaves** and other green parts of the plant.

$$\text{carbon dioxide} + \text{water} \xrightarrow{\text{catalysed by chlorophyll}} \text{sugars} + \text{oxygen}$$

$$6CO_2(g) + 6H_2O\,(l) \rightarrow C_6H_{12}O_6\,(aq) + 6O_2(g)$$

Limiting factors affect the rate of photosynthesis:

- **carbon dioxide** at low concentration limits the rate of photosynthesis whatever the light intensity
- **dim light** limits the rate of photosynthesis even if the level of carbon dioxide remains high
- the higher the **temperature** the faster is the rate of photosynthesis – within limits (> 0°C and < 45°C)
- **lack of water** limits metabolism (including photosynthesis) because water is a solvent for chemical reactions.

See also • p.7 **Metabolism** • p.26 **Chloroplasts**

Inside the leaf

A leaf is **adapted** for photosynthesis.

- **Palisade cells** packed beneath the transparent epidermis are filled with chloroplasts ★ as a result many chloroplasts are exposed to bright light.
- **Spongy mesophyll cells** are loosely packed ★ as a result there are air spaces between them and carbon dioxide and water vapour circulate freely – bringing the raw materials for photosynthesis to the leaf cells.
- **Guard cells** control the size of the opening of the **stoma** ★ as a result the rate of diffusion of gases through the stomata is controlled.
- The cells of the lower leaf surface lack chloroplasts, except the guard cells.

Cross-section of a leaf

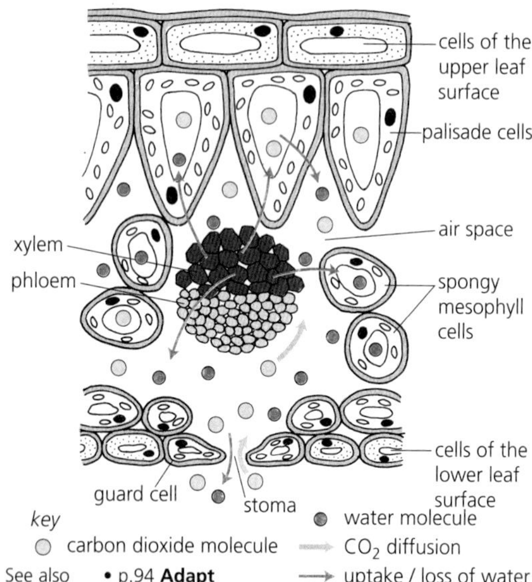

 See also • p.94 **Adapt**

Transport in plants

Xylem tissue transports **water** – **dead** xylem cells form tubes through which water is drawn. The walls of xylem tubes are waterproofed with a substance called **lignin**. **Phloem** tissue transports **food** in flowering plants. **Living** phloem consists of tubes of **sieve cells** and **companion cells**.

The arrangement of xylem and phloem in flowering plants

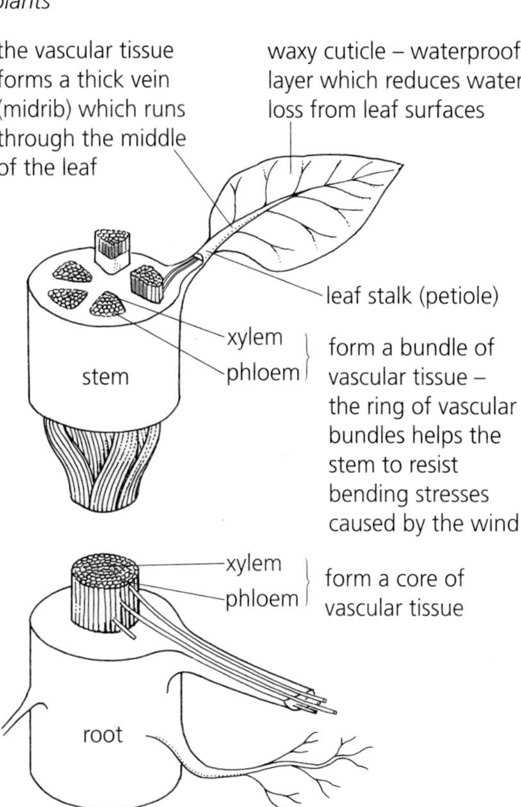

the vascular tissue forms a thick vein (midrib) which runs through the middle of the leaf
waxy cuticle – waterproof layer which reduces water loss from leaf surfaces
leaf stalk (petiole)
xylem
phloem
form a bundle of vascular tissue – the ring of vascular bundles helps the stem to resist bending stresses caused by the wind
stem
xylem
phloem
form a core of vascular tissue
root

Transport of water and minerals

The movement of water and minerals in solution from the soil and through the plant is shown on page 43.

- Root hairs absorb water from the soil by **osmosis**; mineral ions are **actively transported** into the root.
- Water passes **through** the root tissue into the xylem by **osmosis**.
- Water travels through the xylem of the root and stem in unbroken columns – **the transpiration stream**.
- Water moves through the xylem of the leaf stalk and veins of the leaf.
- Water evaporates into the large air spaces within the leaf – the air spaces are saturated with water vapour.
- The concentration of water vapour in the atmosphere is lower than that in the air spaces – water vapour therefore diffuses from the leaf through the stomata; the process is called **transpiration**.
- Water lost by cells through evaporation is replaced with water drawn through the cells by osmosis – cells next to the xylem draw water from the xylem by osmosis.

Plants **lose** water through transpiration and **gain** water through its uptake by the roots. If the loss of water is **greater** than the gain then the stomata close and transpiration is reduced. If the loss of water continues then the cells of the plant lose **turgor** (ridigity) and the plant **wilts**. Different factors **increase** the rate of transpiration:

- **↑ temperature**
- **↓ humidity**
- **↑ wind velocity**
- **↓ light intensity**.

See also • p.40 **Leaf structure** • p.40 **Stomata** • p.27 **Active transport**

Transport of water and minerals – figure

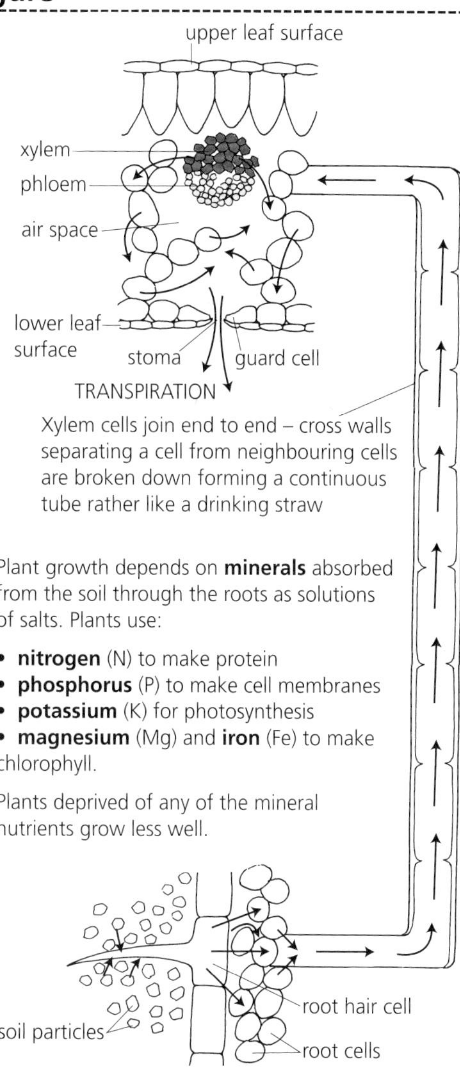

Plant growth depends on **minerals** absorbed from the soil through the roots as solutions of salts. Plants use:

- **nitrogen** (N) to make protein
- **phosphorus** (P) to make cell membranes
- **potassium** (K) for photosynthesis
- **magnesium** (Mg) and **iron** (Fe) to make chlorophyll.

Plants deprived of any of the mineral nutrients grow less well.

Transport of food

The figure on page 45 shows the movement of food from the leaf to all parts of the plant.

- The concentration of sugar in the leaf is often lower than the concentration of sugar in the upper ends of the **sieve tubes**
★ as a result sugar has to move from the leaf into the sieve tubes by **active transport**.
- Osmosis draws water from the xylem and increases the pressure in the sieve tubes
★ as a result sugar solution moves to all parts of the plant through the sieve tubes – the process is called **translocation** – the **companion cells** support the function of sieve cells.
- Pressure in the sieve tubes drops as cells use sugar or store it as starch (e.g. in root cells).

The figure below shows how plants use the sugar made by photosynthesis.

sugars
for respiration
to make starch which is a store of food
to make cellulose which is a component of cell walls
to react with nitrates to form proteins

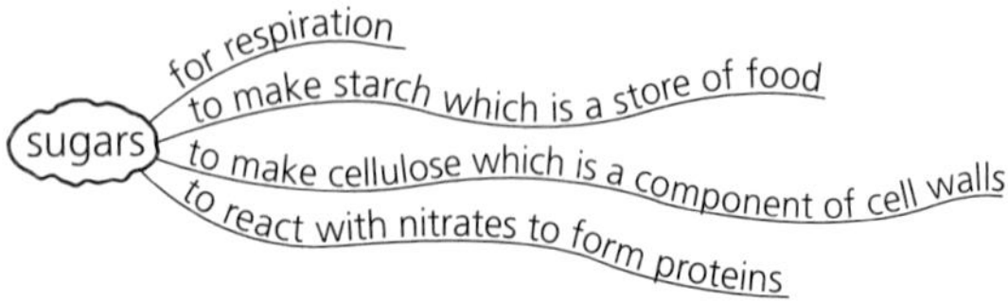

Transport of food – figure

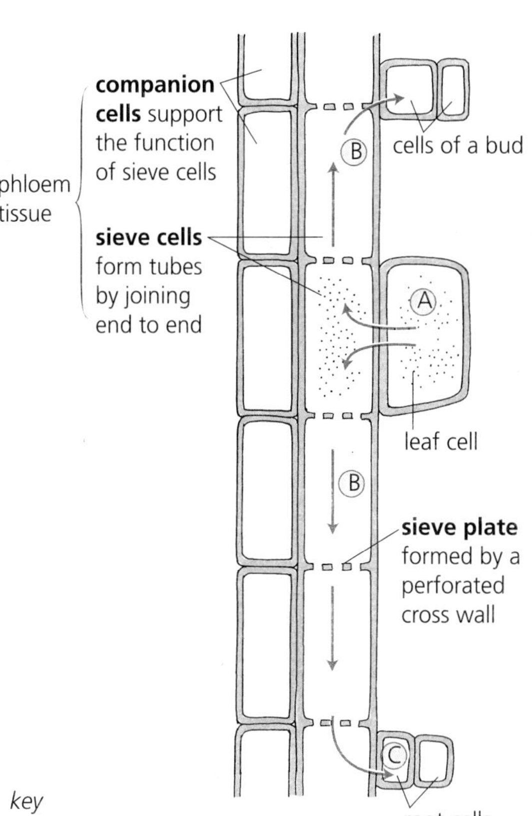

key

- sugar concentration
- → movement of e.g. sugar
- (A) active transport of sugar into sieve cells
- (B) sugar translocation
- (C) conversion of sugar into starch in the root

Plant responses

Plants move by growing in response to stimuli. **Nastic** movements are responses to stimuli that come from **all** directions. **Tropic** movements are responses to stimuli which come mainly from one direction (see page 47). Tropisms are **positive** if the plant grows towards the stimulus and **negative** if it grows away. The growing tips (shoot/root) of a plant are **receptors** for different stimuli.

Auxin is an example of a plant hormone (growth substance). It is produced in the shoot tip and makes the cellulose wall of plant cells more elastic. Cells therefore elongate rapidly. There is more auxin in the shady side of the shoot tip. The cells there grow **more** rapidly than the cells on the brightly lit side. The shoot bends towards the light and receives as much light as possible for photosynthesis.

The effect of the hormone produced by the shoot cap is different from auxin produced by the shoot tip. It **slows down** growth in the underside of the root tip and the root bends down.

Farmers and gardeners use auxin. Synthetic auxin is a **weed killer**. **Auxin paste** smeared over the carpels produces **seedless** fruit without fertilisation. The auxin in **rooting powder** encourages root growth from stem cuttings.

 See also • p.83 **Carpel** • p.84 **Asexual reproduction**

Plant responses – figure

Tropisms – the response of the shoot tip to light and the root cap to gravity and water

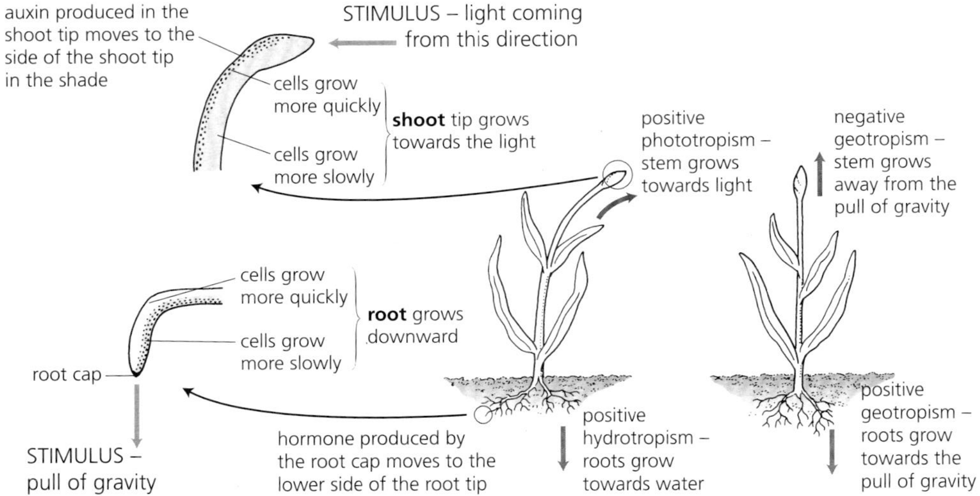

auxin produced in the shoot tip moves to the side of the shoot tip in the shade

STIMULUS – light coming from this direction

cells grow more quickly

cells grow more slowly

shoot tip grows towards the light

positive phototropism – stem grows towards light

negative geotropism – stem grows away from the pull of gravity

cells grow more quickly

cells grow more slowly

root grows downward

root cap

STIMULUS – pull of gravity

hormone produced by the root cap moves to the lower side of the root tip

positive hydrotropism – roots grow towards water

positive geotropism – roots grow towards the pull of gravity

Plants as Organisms

Questions

1 (a) Name the inorganic substances that are the raw materials for photosynthesis. (b) Name the gas given off during photosynthesis.

2 Minerals are needed for healthy growth. Match each substance in column **A** with its function in column **B**.

A substances	**B functions**
Nitrogen	Cell membranes
Phosphorus	Chlorophyll
Magnesium	Protein

3 Compare the characteristics of xylem tissue with those of phloem tissue.

4 List the major limiting factors for photosynthesis. Briefly explain how a greenhouse overcomes the effect of limiting factors on the growth of plants.

5 Match items **A** with the correct descriptions **B**.

A tropisms	**B descriptions**
Phototropism	Gravity
Geotropism	Light
Hydrotropism	Water

Answers

1 (a) carbon dioxide and water (b) oxygen

2

A substances	**B functions**
nitrogen	protein
phosphorus	cell membranes
magnesium	chlorophyll

3 Xylem: dead tissue (cells): tissue (cells) waterproofed with lignin; transports water and minerals; transport of materials is one way: xylem tissue does not have companion cells. **Phloem:** living tissue (cells): tissue (cells) not waterproofed with lignin; transport of materials is both ways; phloem tissue has companion cells.

4 temperature; light intensity; supplies of carbon dioxide; and water / a modern greenhouse provides warmth; lighting; a source of carbon dioxide; and water from sprinkler systems

5

A tropisms	**B descriptions**
phototropism	light
geotropism	gravity
hydrotropism	water

Food

Food is a source of:

- **energy** that powers life's activities
- materials for the **growth** and **repair** of the body
- substances that control the **metabolism** of cells.

The nutrients in food are **carbohydrates**, **fats**, **proteins**, **vitamins** and **minerals**. **Water** and **fibre** are also components of food. **Additives** are put into food.

The **energy value** of food is measured using an instrument called a **bomb calorimeter**. People's energy needs depend on their:

- age • gender (male or female) • activities.

Young people, pregnant and lactating (producing milk) women and active people need the most energy. The **metabolic rate** measures the rate at which the body uses energy. It is lowest (the **basal metabolic rate**) when the body is at rest.

A person's weight depends on the balance between the body's energy **output** (activities) and energy **input** (food intake). If output balances input then a person's weight is **constant**.

Our diet is the food and drink we take in. Choosing items from each of the basic four food groups:

- dairy food
- bread and cereals
- meat and alternatives
- fruit and vegetables

helps provide a **balanced diet**.

See also • p.7 **Metabolism**

Food and diet – Mind Map

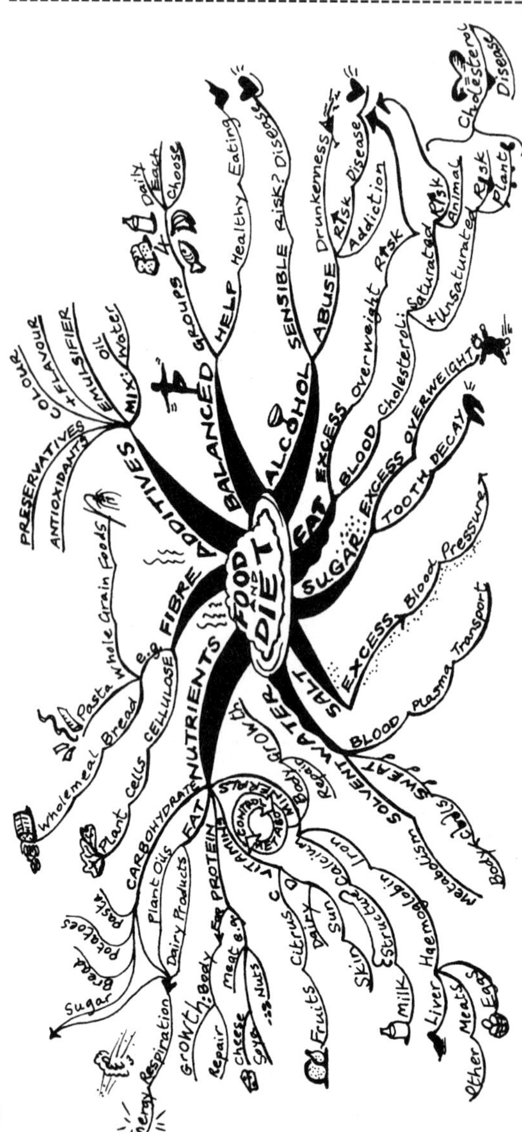

Digesting food

Food is processed through the **intestine**. The muscular action which moves food through the intestine is called **peristalsis**.

- **Ingestion** – food is taken into the mouth.
- **Digestion** – large molecules of food which the body cannot absorb are broken down into smaller molecules which the body can absorb.
- **Absorption** – the small molecules of food pass into the bloodstream.
- **Egestion** – undigested food is removed from the body through the anus.

The **liver** and **pancreas** are connected by ducts. They play an important role in the digestion of food. Digested food is **absorbed** through the wall of the **ileum** (see page 53) into the bloodstream.

The human intestine

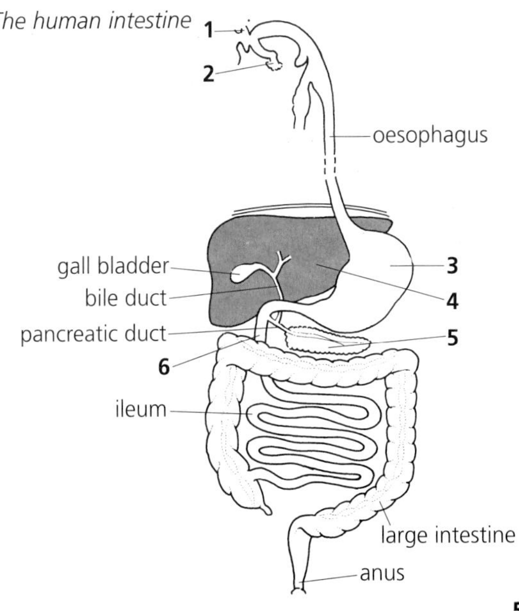

Digesting food – mouth, stomach and small intestine

(M) = mechanical processes break up the food and mix it with digestive juices.
(C) = chemical reactions digest food using different enzymes (see page 54).

1 (M) Teeth chew food, breaking it into small pieces. As a result:

★ the surface area of food exposed to the action of digestive enzymes is increased
★ food is digested more quickly.

2 (C) Saliva, produced by the salivary glands:

- contains the enzyme amylase
- moistens the food – making it easier to swallow.

3 (M) Muscles of the **stomach** wall and **small intestine** mix food thoroughly with different juices containing digestive enzymes.
(C) Gastric juice, produced by **pits** in the stomach wall, contains **hydrochloric acid** and the enzymes **renin** and **pepsin**. Renin makes milk solid so that it stays a longer time in the gut and is digested. **Hydrochloric acid** increases the acidity of the stomach contents. As a result:

★ bacteria in the food are killed
★ the action of salivary amylase is stopped.

4 (C) Bile – produced by the **liver** – is a green alkaline liquid which is stored in the gall bladder before release into the small intestine through the bile duct.

- Bile neutralises acid from the stomach.
- Bile breaks fat into small droplets.

Digesting food – continued

emulsification – increasing the surface area of fat exposed to the action of the enzyme **lipase**.

5 (C) Pancreatic juice – produced by the **pancreas** – is released into the small intestine through the pancreatic duct. It contains:

- **sodium carbonate** which neutralises stomach acid
- **carbohydrases**, **proteases** and **lipases**.

6 (C) Intestinal juice – produced by glands in the wall of the **duodenum** and **ileum** contains:

- **carbohydrases** and **lipases** that complete the digestion of carbohydrates and fats.

The ileum: absorption of digested food

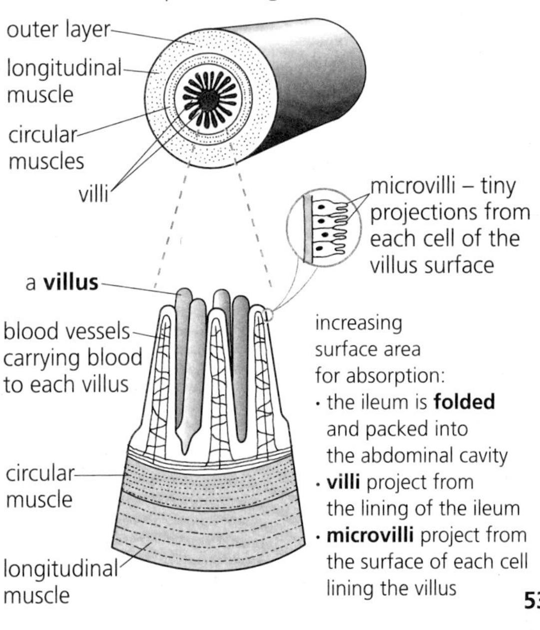
outer layer
longitudinal muscle
circular muscles
villi
microvilli – tiny projections from each cell of the villus surface
a villus
blood vessels carrying blood to each villus
circular muscle
longitudinal muscle
increasing surface area for absorption:
· the ileum is folded and packed into the abdominal cavity
· villi project from the lining of the ileum
· microvilli project from the surface of each cell lining the villus

Digestive enzymes

Enzymes that digest carbohydrates, proteins and fats

Enzyme group	Example	Where found	Food component	After digestion
CARBOHYDRASES (catalyse the digestion of carbohydrates)	Amylase	Mouth	Starch	Maltose
	Maltase	Small intestine	Maltose	Glucose
PROTEASES (catalyse the digestion of proteins)	Pepsin	Stomach	Protein	Polypeptides
	Chymotrypsin Dipeptidase }	Small intestine	Polypeptides Dipeptides	Dipeptides Amino acids
LIPASES (catalyse the digestion of fat)	Lipase	Small intestine	Fat	Fatty acids + glycerol

Using air

Breathing air, gaseous exchange and aerobic respiration are linked processes.

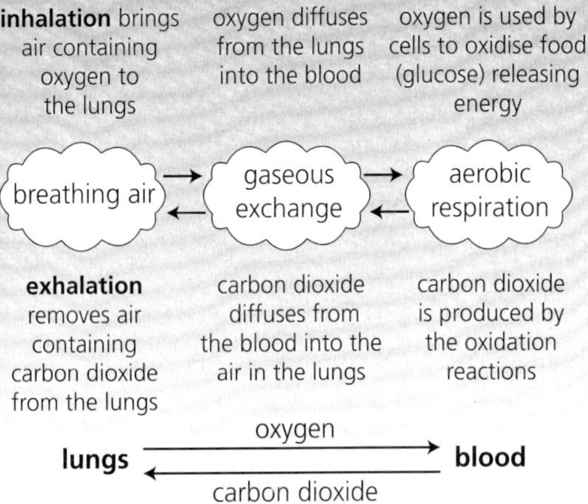
inhalation brings air containing oxygen to the lungs
oxygen diffuses from the lungs into the blood
oxygen is used by cells to oxidise food (glucose) releasing energy
breathing air
gaseous exchange
aerobic respiration
exhalation removes air containing carbon dioxide from the lungs
carbon dioxide diffuses from the blood into the air in the lungs
carbon dioxide is produced by the oxidation reactions
oxygen
lungs
blood
carbon dioxide

The **upper respiratory tract** is a tube from the nostrils and mouth to the lungs (see page 56). It:

- **warms** inhaled air to body temperature
- **cleans** inhaled air of dust particles and disease-causing organisms.

Notice that the **bronchus** branching from the trachea forms a network of small tubes called **bronchioles** in the lungs. The bronchioles divide into even smaller tubes which end in clusters of sac-like structures called **alveoli**.

The lungs and upper respiratory tract

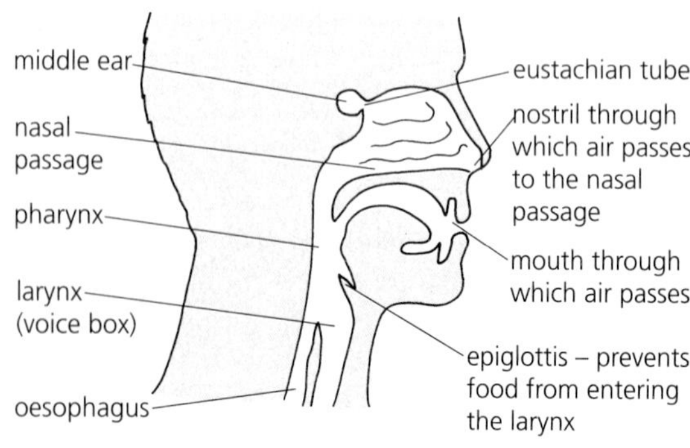

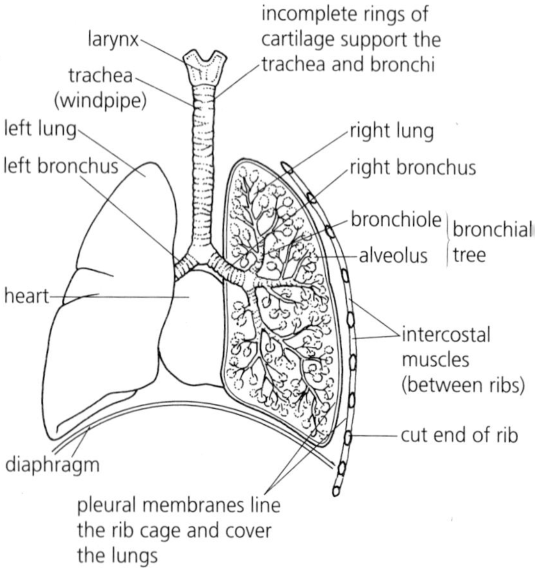

middle ear
nasal passage
pharynx
larynx (voice box)
oesophagus
eustachian tube
nostril through which air passes to the nasal passage
mouth through which air passes
epiglottis – prevents food from entering the larynx

incomplete rings of cartilage support the trachea and bronchi
larynx
trachea (windpipe)
left lung
left bronchus
heart
diaphragm
right lung
right bronchus
bronchiole
alveolus
bronchial tree
intercostal muscles (between ribs)
cut end of rib
pleural membranes line the rib cage and cover the lungs

Gaseous exchange in the lungs

Exchanging gases (oxygen and carbon dioxide) takes place between the walls of the alveoli and the capillary blood vessels. The millions of alveoli in a pair of human lungs form a surface area of about 90m². Each alveolus is adapted for the efficient diffusion of gases. It is:

- thin walled
- moist
- well supplied with blood vessels.

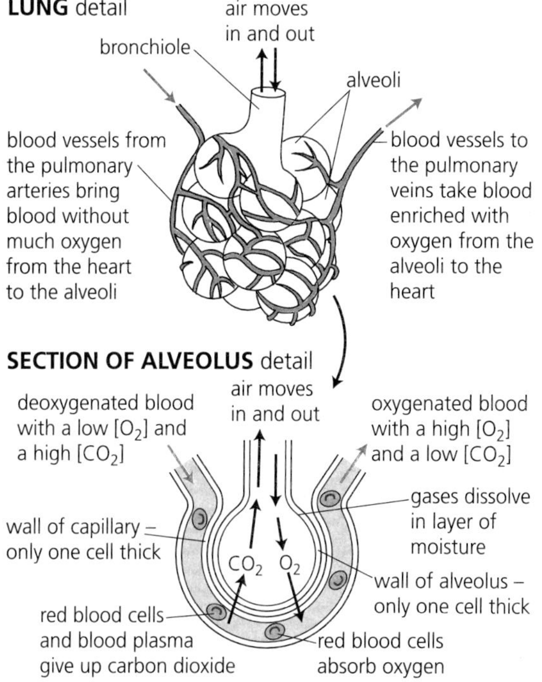
LUNG detail
air moves in and out
bronchiole
alveoli
blood vessels from the pulmonary arteries bring blood without much oxygen from the heart to the alveoli
blood vessels to the pulmonary veins take blood enriched with oxygen from the alveoli to the heart
SECTION OF ALVEOLUS detail
air moves in and out
deoxygenated blood with a low [O_2] and a high [CO_2]
oxygenated blood with a high [O_2] and a low [CO_2]
gases dissolve in layer of moisture
wall of capillary – only one cell thick
CO_2 O_2
wall of alveolus – only one cell thick
red blood cells and blood plasma give up carbon dioxide
red blood cells absorb oxygen

See also • p. 27 **Diffusion** • p. 60 **Plasma**

Breathing movements

The **ribs** and **diaphragm** form an elastic cage around the lungs. As they move, the pressure in the lungs changes. This change in pressure causes **inhaling** – breathing in – and **exhaling** – breathing out.

Inhaling and exhaling

inhaling the volume of the thoracic cavity increases – the pressure of air inside the thoracic cavity becomes less than atmospheric pressure – so air is drawn into the lungs

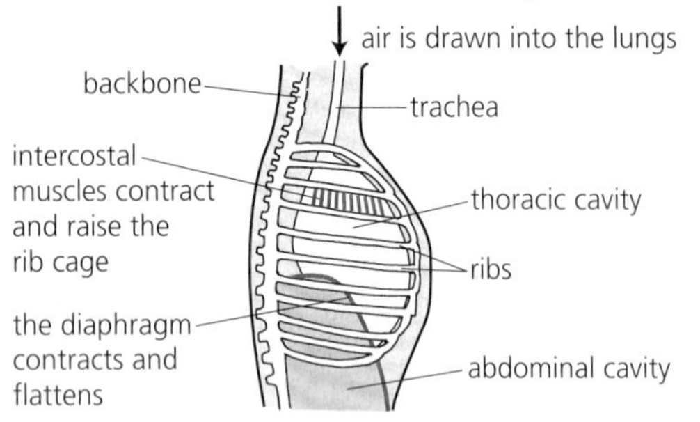

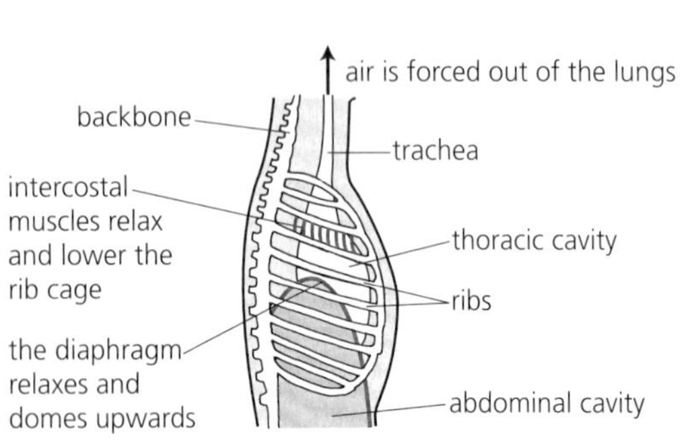

exhaling the volume of the thoracic cavity decreases - the pressure of air inside the thoracic cavity becomes greater than atmospheric pressure so air is forced out of the lungs

Respiration

The **oxidation** of digested food substances in cells releases energy (**cellular respiration**). The energy released powers the activities which define the characteristics of life. Cellular respiration that uses oxygen is called **aerobic respiration** and occurs in the **mitochondria** of cells.

Glucose + Oxygen → Carbon dioxide + Water

$C_6H_{12}O_6(aq) + 6O_2(g) \rightarrow 6CO_2(g) + 6H_2O(l)$

Energy released = 16.1 kJ/g glucose.

Cellular respiration that does not use oxygen is called **anaerobic respiration** and occurs in the **cytoplasm** of cells.

When muscles are contracting vigorously.

- Glucose → Lactic acid
- $C_6H_{12}O_6(aq) \rightarrow 2CH_3CHOHCO_2(aq)$
- Energy released = 0.83kJ/g glucose.

Lactic acid accumulates and an **oxygen debt** builds up. Too much lactic acid stops the muscles from working. **Panting** brings a rush of oxygen to the muscles. The lactic acid is oxidised and the oxygen debt **repaid**.

In yeast cells in the absence of oxygen.

- Glucose → Ethanol + Carbon dioxide
- $C_6H_{12}O_6(aq) \rightarrow 2C_2H_5OH(aq) + 2CO_2(g)$
- Energy released = 1.17kJ/g glucose.

Notice that the energy released during anaerobic respiration is less than in aerobic respiration. Cells do not use the energy released directly. It is converted into the energy of chemical bonds in a substance called **adenosine triphosphate** (ATP). Anaerobic respiration in yeast cells provides us with food and drink:

- ethanol is the 'alcohol' in wines and beers
- carbon dioxide puffs up bread making it rise before baking.

See also • p. 7 **Characteristics of life** • p. 57 **Gaseous exchange**
• p. 26 **Mitochondria** • p. 26 **Cytoplasm**

Blood

Blood is a liquid containing different cells. The liquid is called **plasma** which consists of 90% water and 10% of materials dissolved in it:

- **blood proteins** including antibodies that defend the body against disease; fibrinogen which helps stop bleeding and enzymes
- **foods** and **vitamins**
- **hormones** which help co-ordinate different body functions.

Red blood cells are made in bone **marrow**. They have **no** nucleus and are packed with the pigment **haemoglobin** which gives them their red colour. Haemoglobin combines with the oxygen which diffuses from the alveoli into the bloodstream. Old red blood cells are destroyed in the liver.

White blood cells are made in the **bone marrow** and **spleen**. They do have a nucleus. There are two basic types:

- **lymphocytes** which produce **antibodies** that destroy substances/cells the body does not recognise as its own – **antigens**
- **phagocytes** that engulf substances/cells attacked by antibodies.

Platelets which look like fragments of red cells. They help to stop bleeding.

Blood cells seen under a microscope

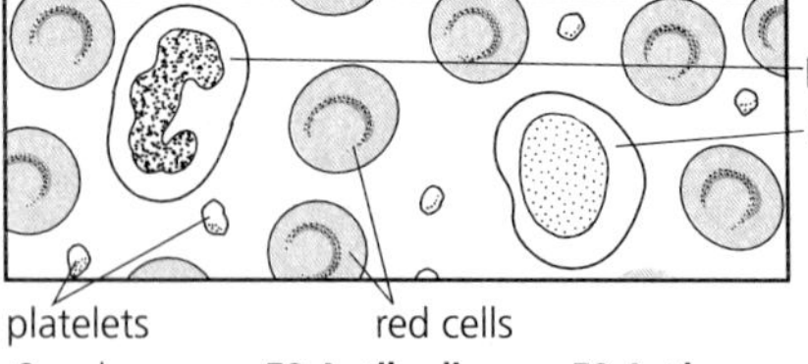

 See also • p. 79 **Antibodies** • p. 79 **Antigens** • p. 57 **Alveoli** • p. 52 **Liver**

Moving blood around

The blood system consists of tube-like vessels – **arteries**, **veins** and **capillaries** – through which blood is pumped around the body by the **heart**.

EXAM HINT – make sure that you can trace the flow of blood through the heart.

Blood system

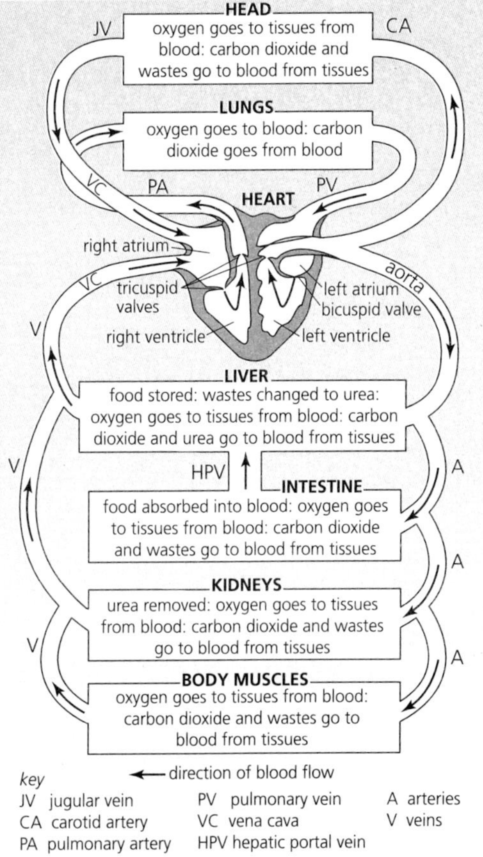

HEAD
oxygen goes to tissues from blood: carbon dioxide and wastes go to blood from tissues
JV
CA
LUNGS
oxygen goes to blood: carbon dioxide goes from blood
VC
PA
PV
HEART
right atrium
aorta
VC
tricuspid valves
left atrium
bicuspid valve
V
right ventricle
left ventricle
LIVER
food stored: wastes changed to urea: oxygen goes to tissues from blood: carbon dioxide and urea go to blood from tissues
V
HPV
A
INTESTINE
food absorbed into blood: oxygen goes to tissues from blood: carbon dioxide and wastes go to blood from tissues
A
KIDNEYS
urea removed: oxygen goes to tissues from blood: carbon dioxide and wastes go to blood from tissues
V
A
BODY MUSCLES
oxygen goes to tissues from blood: carbon dioxide and wastes go to blood from tissues
key
← direction of blood flow
JV jugular vein
CA carotid artery
PA pulmonary artery
PV pulmonary vein
VC vena cava
HPV hepatic portal vein
A arteries
V veins

Blood vessels

- **Arteries** carry blood from the heart – the blood transports oxygen, (except the pulmonary artery) digested food and other substances to the tissues and organs that need them.
- **Veins** carry blood to the heart – the blood transports carbon dioxide (except the pulmonary vein) and other wastes produced by the metabolism of cells from the tissues and organs.
- **Capillaries** link arteries with veins – the exchange of materials between blood and the tissues and organs occurs through the walls of the capillaries.

Comparing arteries and veins

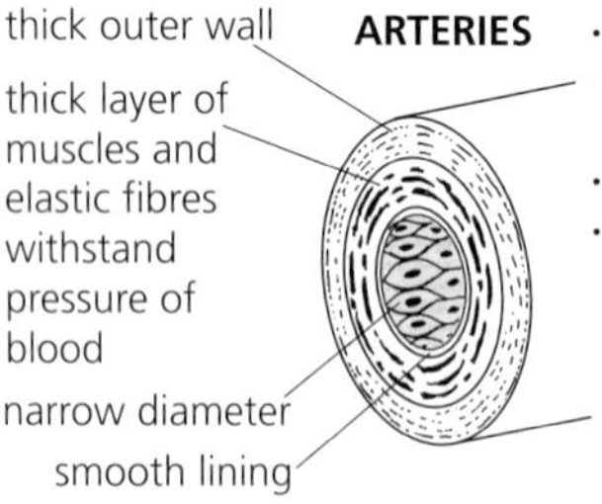

ARTERIES

thick outer wall

thick layer of muscles and elastic fibres withstand pressure of blood

narrow diameter

smooth lining

- carry blood away from the heart to organs and tissues
- blood at high pressure
- have a pulse because the vessel walls expand and relax as blood spurts from the heart

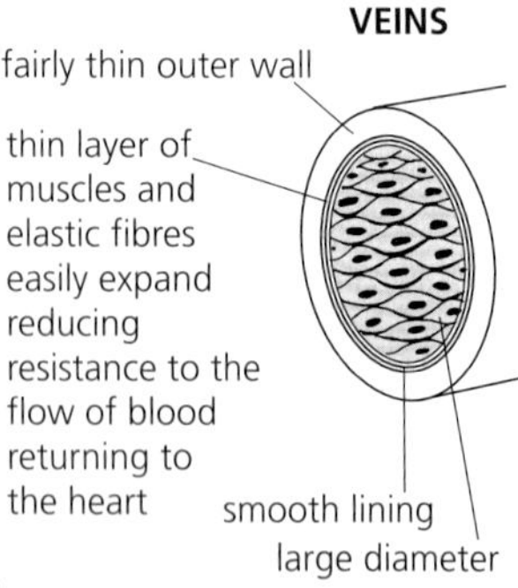

VEINS

fairly thin outer wall

thin layer of muscles and elastic fibres easily expand reducing resistance to the flow of blood returning to the heart

smooth lining

large diameter

- return blood to the heart from organs and tissues (except hepatic portal veir
- blood at low pressure
- working body muscles squeeze the veins helping push blood to the heart
- do not have a pulse since blood flows smoothly
- have valves which ensure that blood flows in one direction only returning to the heart

Capillaries

Capillaries are tiny blood vessels, 0.001 mm in diameter. They form dense networks in the tissues of the body.

- The walls of capillary blood vessels are one cell thick ★ as a result substances easily diffuse between blood in the capillaries and the surrounding tissues.
- No cell is very far away from a capillary.
- The blood in capillaries supplies nearby cells with oxygen, food and other substances – it also carries away carbon dioxide and other wastes produced by the cells' metabolism.
- **Tissue fluid** carries oxygen, food and other substances to the cells – this fluid is blood plasma that has been forced out through the thin capillary walls by the pressure of the blood inside.
- Red blood cells squeeze through the smallest capillaries in single file ★ as a result the pressure drops as blood passes through the capillaries from the artery to the vein.

Capillaries at work

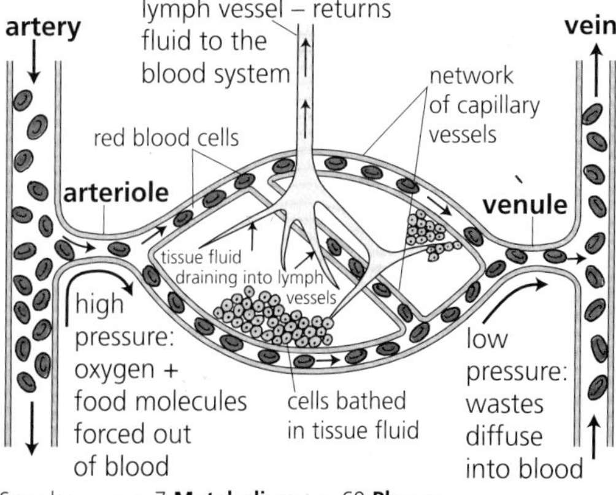

See also • p. 7 **Metabolism** • p. 60 **Plasma**

Disorders of the blood

Leukaemia is the overproduction of abnormal white blood cells. ★ As a result, red blood cell production is lowered.
Treatment is with drugs that slow the production of white blood cells and radiotherapy which kills the abnormal cells.

Haemophilia is a genetic disease. The blood does not clot properly because factor VIII – one of the substances in the blood needed for blood clots to form – is missing. ★ As a result, **haemophiliacs** (people suffering from haemophilia) lose a lot of blood if they injure themselves.
Treatment is by injection of factor VIII.

AIDS (**A**cquired **I**mmune **D**eficiency **S**yndrome) is caused by the **H**uman **I**mmunodeficiency **V**irus (**HIV**). The virus attacks a particular type of lymphocyte. ★ As a result, a person infected with HIV has reduced protection from disease-causing microorganisms.

 See also • p. 60 **Lymphocyte**

Disorders of the blood – understanding heart disease

The build-up of fatty deposits called **atheroma** in the **coronary arteries** is one cause of **heart disease**. It increases the risk of blood clots forming. A blood clot in the coronary arteries can interrupt the blood supply to the heart and the person suffers a **heart attack**. The symptoms are:

- severe pain in the chest, neck and arms
- sweating
- faintness and sickness.

The clot is called a **thrombus** and the blockage a **thrombosis**.

The risk of heart disease

BLOOD SUPPLY TO THE HEART

about 100 000 people in the UK die each year of heart disease

THE PROBLEM

RISK FACTORS

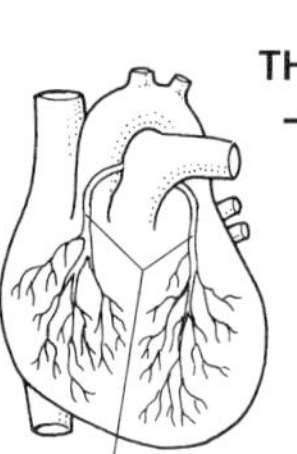

coronary arteries supply food and oxygen to the heart muscle

coronary arteries branch off dorsal aorta

UNAVOIDABLE

- the risk of heart disease increases with age
- men are more at risk than women
- the tendency to develop heart disease can run in families

AVOIDABLE

- overweight people are more at risk
- people with high levels of cholesterol in the blood are more at risk
- permanently raised blood pressure increases the risk of heart disease and stroke
- the more stress a person suffers, the greater the risk of heart disease

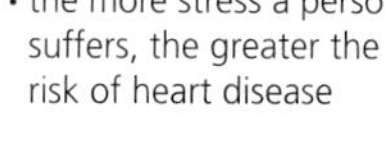

Co-ordination and the nervous system

A **stimulus** is a change in the environment which causes a living organism to take action. A **response** is the action that the organism takes. The nervous system links stimuli and responses. The process runs as follows.

stimulus →	**receptor →**	**nerves →**	**effector →**	**response**
	detects stimulus converting it into nerve impulses	transmit nerve impulses	muscles or glands which respond to nerve impulses	

Human nervous system

Neurones (nerve cells) are specialised to transmit nerve impulses. Each neurone consists of a **cell body** and **axon** which is surrounded by a sheath of fatty material called **myelin**. Bundles of neurones form **nerves** that build the nervous system.

A **reflex arc** is the chain of neurones along which nerve impulses travel to bring about a reflex (automatic) response to a stimulus (see page 67). A tiny gap called a **synapse** separates each neurone from the next neurone in the chain.

Neurotransmitter released from the end of one neurone diffuses across the synapse and stimulates the next neurone to fire off new nerve impulses.

Cross-section through the nerve cord

1 sensory receptor detects stimulus and converts it into nerve impulses
ascending fibre carries nerve impulses to the brain
2 sensory neurone carries nerve impulses from the sensory receptor to the spinal cord
cell body
TO THE BRAIN
3 relay neurone receives nerve impulses from the sensory neurone and passes them to the motor neurone
synapse
axon
descending fibre carries nerve impulses from the brain
5 muscle fibres contract when stimulated by the arrival of nerve impulses – if you step on a drawing pin the leg muscles contract lifting your foot out of harm's way
4 motor neurone receives nerve impulses from the relay neurone and passes them to the effector muscle

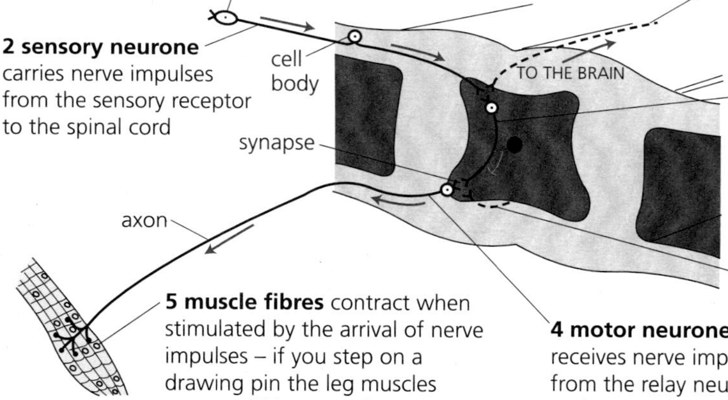

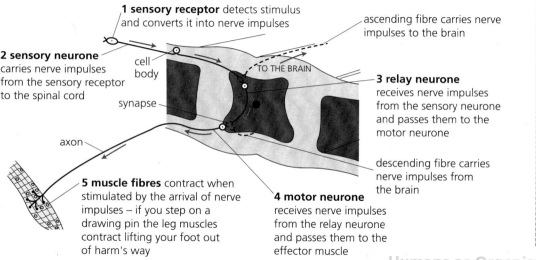

Hormones

Hormones are chemicals which regulate the activities of the body. They are produced in the tissues of the **endocrine glands** which are ductless glands that release their hormones directly into the blood stream. The tissue on which a particular hormone(s) acts is called the **target tissue**.

Human endocrine glands and their hormones

pituitary gland at base of the brain produces different hormones which affect:

- water reabsorption from the kidney tubules (ADH)
- sperm and egg productic
- growth
- release of hormones by other endocrine glands

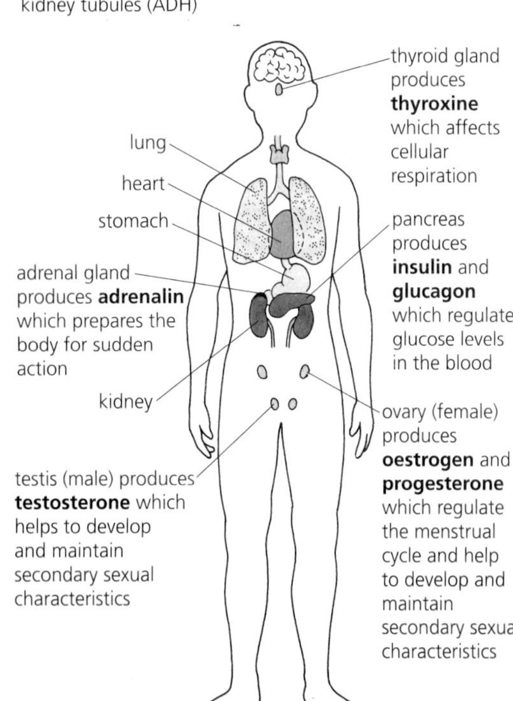
thyroid gland produces **thyroxine** which affects cellular respiration
lung
heart
stomach
pancreas produces **insulin** and **glucagon** which regulate glucose levels in the blood
adrenal gland produces **adrenalin** which prepares the body for sudden action
kidney
ovary (female) produces **oestrogen** and **progesterone** which regulate the menstrual cycle and help to develop and maintain secondary sexua characteristics
testis (male) produces **testosterone** which helps to develop and maintain secondary sexual characteristics

The menstrual cycle

The figure shows the action of the different hormones that control:

- the development and release of an egg from the human ovary
- the changes in the lining of the uterus.

The different events are the components of the **menstrual cycle** and usually occur every month during the years when a woman is fertile (approximately between ages 12–50 years).

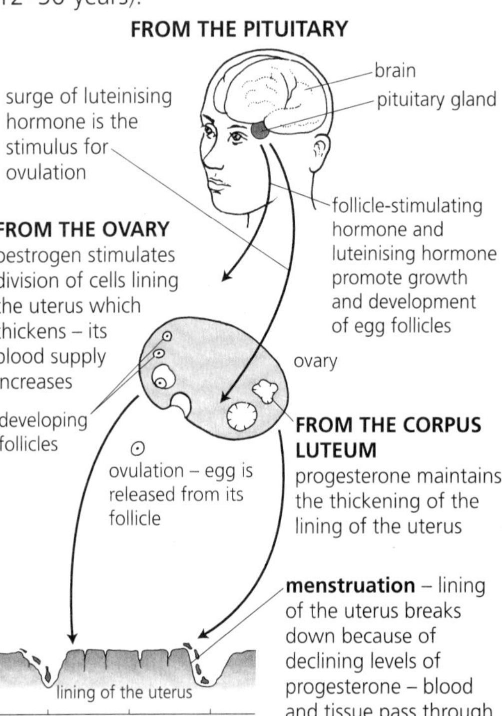
FROM THE PITUITARY
brain
pituitary gland
surge of luteinising hormone is the stimulus for ovulation
follicle-stimulating hormone and luteinising hormone promote growth and development of egg follicles
FROM THE OVARY
oestrogen stimulates division of cells lining the uterus which thickens – its blood supply increases
ovary
developing follicles
FROM THE CORPUS LUTEUM
progesterone maintains the thickening of the lining of the uterus
ovulation – egg is released from its follicle
menstruation – lining of the uterus breaks down because of declining levels of progesterone – blood and tissue pass through the vagina
lining of the uterus
0
14
28 days

Regulating glucose

The hormones **insulin** and **glucagon** help regulate the level of glucose (sugar) in the blood.

- High concentrations of blood glucose promote the release of insulin.
- Low concentrations of blood glucose promote the release of glucagon.

★ As a result the concentration of glucose is regulated at around 90 mg of glucose per 100 cm^3 of blood.

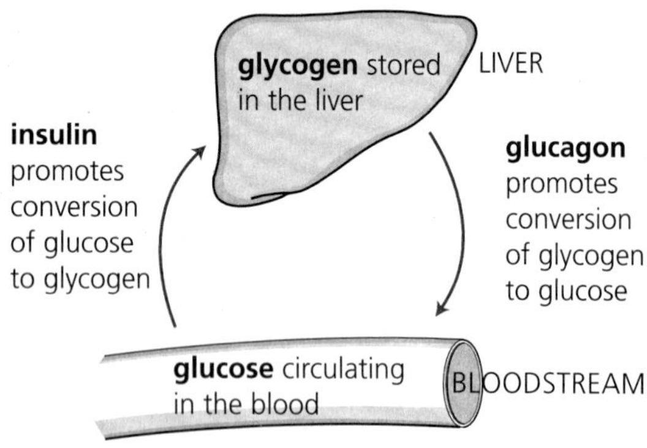

Flight or fight

The hormone **adrenalin** is released in response to sudden shock. It prepares the body for sudden action:

- cells metabolise glucose faster ★ as a result more energy is available for sudden action
- the heart beats more rapidly ★ as a result more blood with its load of glucose reaches tissues and organs more rapidly
- blood is diverted to tissues such as the muscles and brain.

 See also • p. 33 **Glycogen** • p. 7 **Metabolism**

Homeostasis

Keeping conditions in the body constant is called **homeostasis**.

The kidneys at work

Each kidney (see page 72) consists of about one million tiny tubules called **nephrons**. Each nephron (see page 73) is the structure that brings about homeostatic control of the:

- concentration of salts in the body
- water content of the body.

The nephron also excretes urea and other wastes from the body.

Controlling the body's water content

- **Sensory receptors** in the brain detect how much water is in the blood.
- The **pituitary gland** at the base of the brain produces **anti-diuretic hormone** (ADH) which affects the permeability of the walls of the collecting duct of the nephron.

Lots of water in the body:

- Production of ADH from the pituitary gland is reduced ★ as a result most of the surplus water is excreted through the kidneys.

Less water in the body:

- Production of ADH from the pituitary gland is increased ★ as a result the walls of the collecting duct of the nephron are more permeable ('leaky') to water and water is absorbed back into the body.

Where does urea come from?

- **Amino acids** in excess of the body's needs are broken down in the liver.
- The process is called **deamination**.
- **Urea** is formed and excreted in the urine.

See also • p. 68 **Hormones** • p. 34 **Amino acids and proteins**

Kidneys

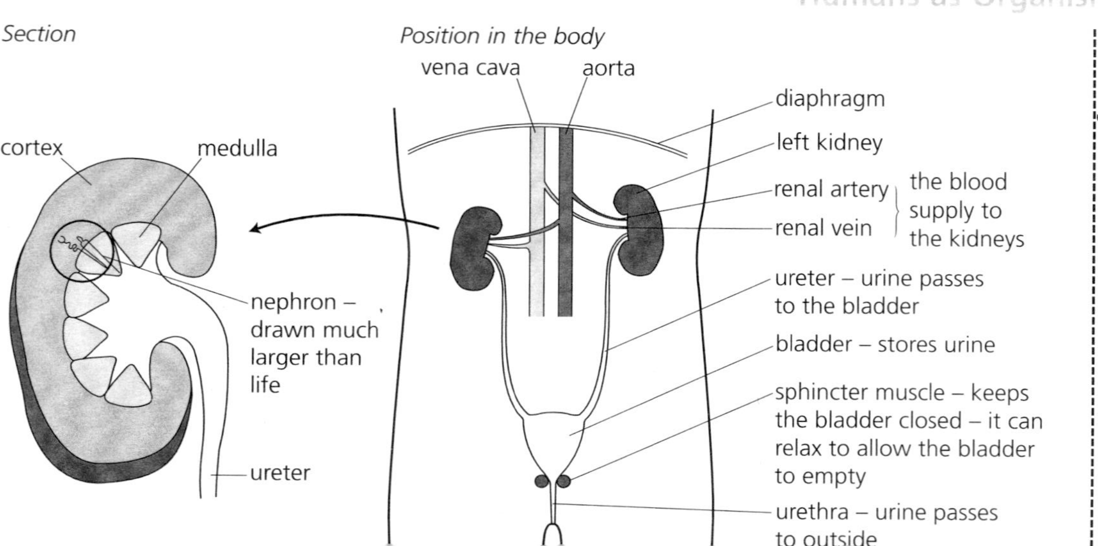
Section
cortex
medulla
nephron – drawn much larger than life
ureter
Position in the body
vena cava
aorta
diaphragm
left kidney
renal artery
renal vein
the blood supply to the kidneys
ureter – urine passes to the bladder
bladder – stores urine
sphincter muscle – keeps the bladder closed – it can relax to allow the bladder to empty
urethra – urine passes to outside

The working nephron

branch from renal artery brings 'dirty' blood under high pressure

glomerulus (knot of capillary blood vessels)

Bowman's capsule (horseshoe shape)

2 reabsorption – glucose, salts and other useful substances pass in solution back into the blood

branch from renal vein takes 'clean' blood away

cortex

medulla

remaining liquid – urine – flows into the ureter

collecting duct

◄- - - - direction of liquid through the nephron

1 filtration – occurs in the **Bowman's capsule** – high pressure blood flow forces waste materials, glucose, salts and other materials in solution through the walls of the capillaries (**glomerulus**) into the Bowman's capsule

3 reabsorption – water passes from the **collecting duct** of the nephron into the blood – the amount of water reabsorbed depends on the amount **anti-diuretic hormone** (ADH) circulating in the blood

See also • pp. 68 and 71 **Anti-diuretic hormone (ADH)**

The skin and control of body temperature

The skin regulates the body's temperature.

- **Hairs** raised by erector muscles trap a layer of air which insulates the body in cold weather (air is a poor conductor of heat); in warm weather the hair is lowered and no air is trapped.
- **Fat** insulates the body and reduces heat loss.
- **Sweat** cools the body because it carries heat energy away from the body as it evaporates.
- Millions of temperature-sensitive sense receptors cover the skin; nerves connect receptor stimuli to the brain – the brain controls the body's response to changes in environmental temperature.
- When it is warm, blood vessels in the skin dilate – **vasodilation** – more blood flows through the vessels in the skin therefore heat is lost to the environment; in cold weather the blood vessels in the skin constrict – **vasoconstriction** – and less heat is lost to the environment.

 See also • p. 67 **Receptors**

Section through the skin

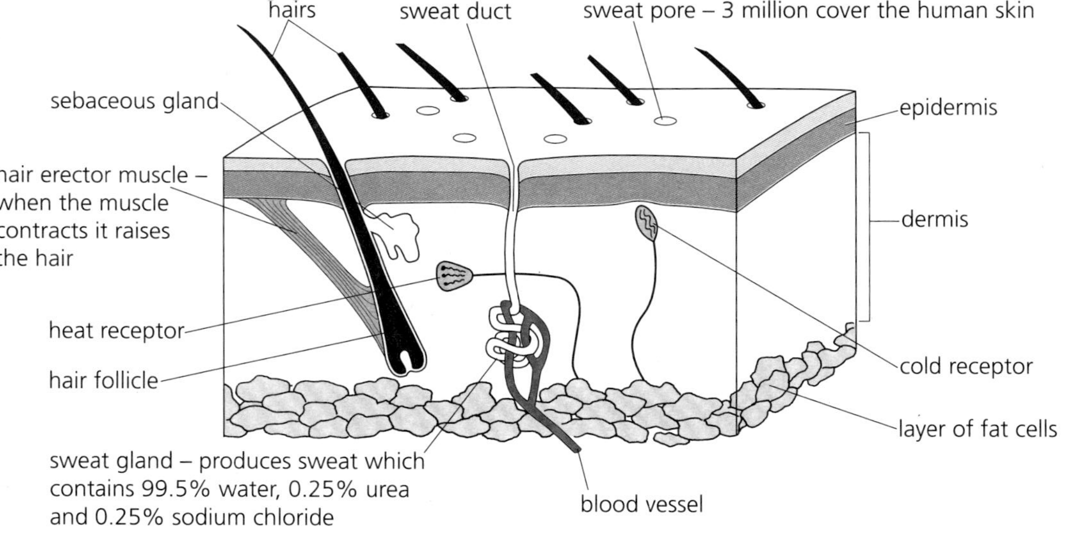

hairs
sweat duct
sweat pore – 3 million cover the human skin
sebaceous gland
epidermis
hair erector muscle – when the muscle contracts it raises the hair
dermis
heat receptor
hair follicle
cold receptor
layer of fat cells
sweat gland – produces sweat which contains 99.5% water, 0.25% urea and 0.25% sodium chloride
blood vessel

Reproduction – Mind Map

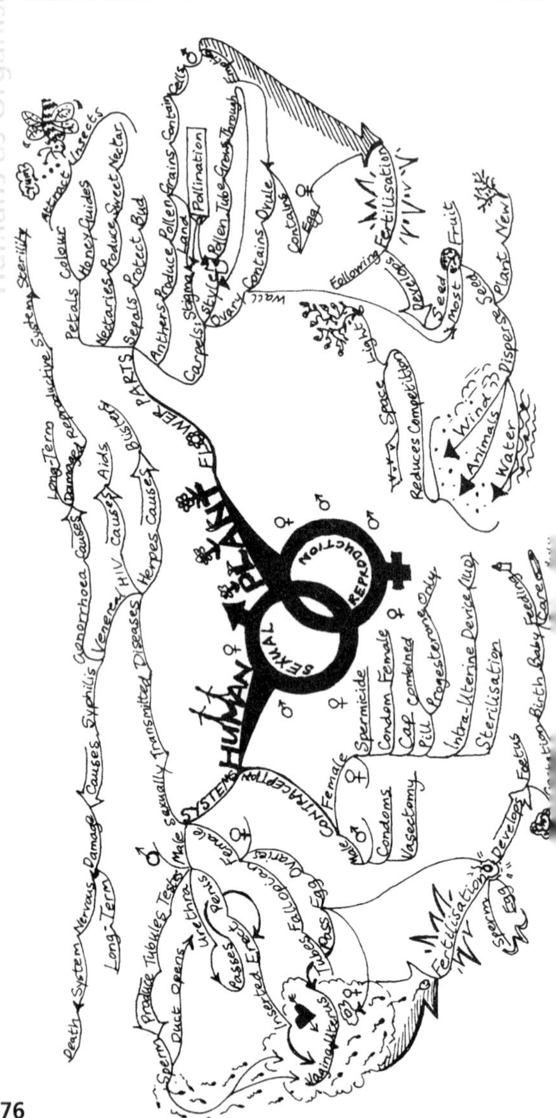

What is disease?

Infectious diseases are caused by a range of organisms which pass from person to person:

- **bacteria**, e.g. cholera, typhoid fever, tuberculosis
- **viruses**, e.g. AIDS, 'flu, German measles
- **fungi**, e.g. thrush, athlete's foot, ringworm
- **protists**, e.g. malaria, sleeping sickness.

Non-infectious diseases develop because the body is not working properly:

- **cancer** – uncontrolled cell division leads to the development of a cancerous growth (tumour)
- **degenerative illnesses** – organs and tissues work less well with wear and tear, e.g. joints become arthritic
- **allergies** – reactions to substances which are normally harmless, e.g. hayfever
- **deficiency** – inadequate intake of vitamins and other essential substances, e.g. scurvy (deficiency of vitamin C).

Genetic diseases result from genetic defects and may be inherited. Genetic make-up also influences our vulnerability to other diseases such as diabetes and heart disease.

- **Down's syndrome** is caused by an extra copy of chromosome 21.
- **Sickle-cell anaemia** is caused by a mutation of the gene – **allele** – controlling the synthesis of the blood pigment haemoglobin.
- **Haemophilia** is caused by the mutation of an allele on the X chromosome.

See also • p. 9 **Bacteria, fungi, protists** • p. 49 **Vitamins** • p. 92 **Mutation** • p. 85 **Alleles**

Lifestyles and disease

Cigarette smoke contains various substances harmful to health.

- **Nicotine** increases the heart rate and blood pressure.
- **Carbon monoxide** combines 300 times more readily with haemoglobin than oxygen does ★ as a result, the level of oxygen in the blood is reduced.
- Tar contains many compounds which cause cancer **(carcinogens)**.

Smoking cigarettes is a major cause of **lung cancer** and **heart disease**. Some substances in cigarette smoke irritate the membrane lining the upper respiratory tract.

- Extra mucus (phlegm) forms in the trachea and bronchi ★ as a result 'smokers cough' may destroy the walls of the alveoli causing **emphysema** – the affected person easily becomes breathless.
- Particles and microorganisms enter the lungs increasing the risk of infection.

Other substances in cigarette smoke stop the **cilia** lining the upper respiratory tract from beating.
Some **drugs** are highly **addictive** and may be **abused** (e.g. cocaine, heroin). This means they are used for non-medical purposes.
Alcohol (ethanol in beers, wine and spirits) depresses the activity of the nervous system. It affects areas of the brain which control judgement.
Solvents in glues, paints, nail varnish and cleaning fluids (dry cleaners) readily produce a vapour at room temperature. Breathing them in gives a warm sense of well-being but also produces dangerous disorientation.

 See also • p.55 **Upper respiratory tract**

Fighting disease

The body's natural defences against disease are:

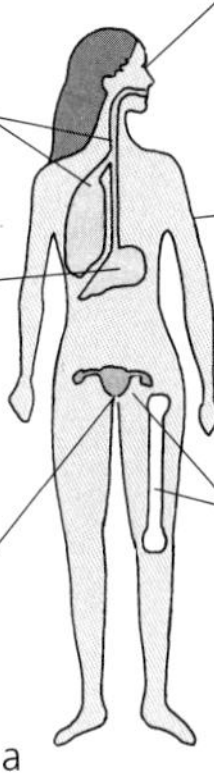

mucus – lines the upper respiratory tract – traps bacteria and particles and is swept away by cilia

tears – contain the enzyme lysozyme which destroys bacteria

skin – glands produce an oily substance called sebum which kills bacteria and fungi

stomach – glands produce hydrochloric acid which kills bacteria on food

white blood cells – are produced in the bone marrow and lymph glands – they destroy bacteria and other organisms which cause disease

cervix – (part of the female reproductive system) – is plugged with mucus which is a barrier to microorganisms

White blood cells

Two types of white blood cell, **lymphocytes** and **phagocytes**, protect the body. They destroy bacteria, viruses or other cells or substances which may cause disease and which the body does not recognise as its own. Such materials 'foreign' to the body are called **antigens**.

- **B-lymphocytes** produce **antibodies** which are proteins that attack **antigens** – antibodies produced against a particular antigen will attack only that antigen; the antibody is said to be **specific** to that antigen.
- **T-lymphocytes** are also specific in their action – they do not produce antigens but instead bind with an antigen and destroy it.

Phagocytes engulf and destroy antigens (see page 80). Some phagocytes pass through tissue to attack antigens that have entered the body through cuts or scratches causing an **inflammatory response**.

Fighting disease – continued

B-lymphocytes produce antibodies; phagocytes engulf bacteria

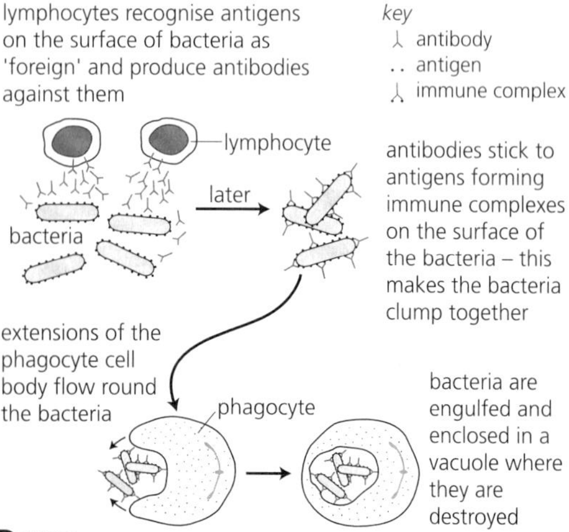

lymphocytes recognise antigens on the surface of bacteria as 'foreign' and produce antibodies against them

key
antibody
antigen
immune complex

lymphocyte

later

bacteria

antibodies stick to antigens forming immune complexes on the surface of the bacteria – this makes the bacteria clump together

extensions of the phagocyte cell body flow round the bacteria

phagocyte

bacteria are engulfed and enclosed in a vacuole where they are destroyed

Drugs

Drugs are used to help in the fight against disease. For example:

- **Antibiotics** are used to attack the different types of bacteria that cause disease.
- **Analgesics** are drugs that reduce pain (painkillers).

Hygiene

- **Disinfectants** are chemicals that kill microorganisms – they are used to keep surfaces (e.g. in the kitchen and bathroom) clean and free from microorganisms.
- **Antiseptics** are usually weaker than disinfectants – they are used to clean wounds or an area of the skin before hypodermic injection.

Humans as Organisms

Questions

1 Match each enzyme in column **A** with its role in digestion in column **B**.

A enzymes	**B roles** digests:
Amylase	Maltose to glucose
Pepsin	Fat to fatty acids and glycerol
Lipase	Starch to maltose
Maltase	Protein to polypeptides

2 Briefly explain (a) Why raised body hair helps us keep warm? (b) Why sweating helps us keep cool?

3 The components of the reflex arc are listed as follows: **sensory neurone, effector, relay neurone, receptor, motor neurone**. Write the components in their correct order.

4 The structures of the kidney tubule and its blood supply are listed below. Rewrite them in the order in which a molecule of urea passes from the renal artery to the outside of the body: **tubule, urethra, bladder, glomerulus, Bowman's capsule, ureter, collecting duct**.

5 What are hormones and how are they transported around the body?

Answers

1

A enzymes	**B roles** digests:
amylase	starch to maltose
pepsin	protein to polypeptides
lipase	fat to fatty acids and glycerol
maltase	maltose to glucose

2 (a) raised hairs trap a layer of air which insulates the body in cold weather / air is a poor conductor of heat (b) sweat cools the body because it carries heat energy away from the body as it evaporates **3** receptor sensory neurone relay neurone motor neurone effector **4** glomerulus Bowman's capsule tubule collecting duct ureter bladder urethra **5** hormones are chemical substances which circulate in the blood

Reproduction

There are two types of reproduction. Each type passes genetic material on from parent(s) to offspring.

In **sexual reproduction** two parents (male and female) each produce sex cells. The male produces sperm; the female produces eggs. Sperm and eggs are formed by **meiosis**. During fertilisation sperm and egg fuse, forming a **zygote**. The zygote divides repeatedly by **mitosis**, producing a ball of cells called an **embryo** which develops into the new individual. The figure below shows the process in humans.

Development of the zygote

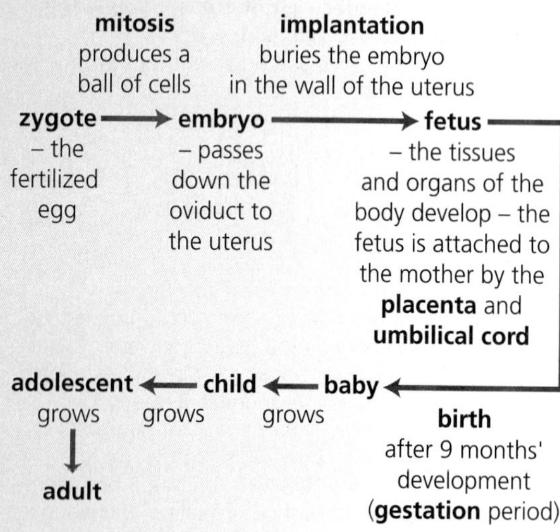
mitosis
produces a ball of cells
implantation
buries the embryo in the wall of the uterus
zygote
– the fertilized egg
embryo
– passes down the oviduct to the uterus
fetus
– the tissues and organs of the body develop – the fetus is attached to the mother by the placenta and umbilical cord
adolescent
child
baby
grows
grows
grows
adult
birth
after 9 months' development (gestation period)

 See also • p. 31 **Meiosis** • p. 31 **Mitosis** • p. 30 **Daughter cells** • p. 92 **Variation**

Reproduction – continued

Sexual reproduction in flowering plants

In flowering plants sexual reproduction involves **pollination, fertilisation** and the formation of **fruits** and **seeds**. The figure below shows the sequence.

pollination
is the transfer of pollen from the anther to the stigma

cross-pollination
is the transfer of pollen between anthers and stigma(s) of different plants

self-pollination
is the transfer of pollen between anthers and stigma(s) on the same plant

fertilization
is the fusion of a male sex nucleus with the female egg nucleus – the male sex nucleus passes down the **pollen tube** which grows from a pollen grain through the **carpel** (stigma → style → ovary)

↓

seed
is formed from the fertilized egg – it contains the embryo plant with its food store; the **fruit** (usually formed from the wall of the ovary) surrounds and protects the seed

The offspring formed by sexual reproduction inherit genes from each parent. They are therefore genetically **different** from one another and their parents. The genetic differences are an important source of **variation**.

Reproduction - continued

Flowers are adapted for pollination:

- insect-pollinated flowers are brightly coloured and produce nectar and scent to attract insect visitors
- wind-pollinated flowers are often a dull colour and are adapted to distribute large quantities of pollen far and wide.

Fruits and seeds are adapted for distribution by either animals or wind.

Asexual reproduction:

One parent divides by mitosis to produce daughter cells which form new individuals, These offspring are genetically **identical** to one another and to their parent. Variation between individuals is therefore limited to genetic changes which are the result of mutation. Methods of asexual reproduction are:

- **fission** – the parent cell divides into equal parts
- **budding** – outgrowth's (buds) of the parent's body separate from the parent – each one becomes a separate individual
- **vegetative parts** of the parent body grow into new individuals, e.g. stems sprout roots and grow into new plants
- **regeneration** – pieces of the parent body grow into new individuals
- **parthenogenesis** – the unfertilised egg develops into a new individual.

Monohybrid inheritance

The study of how offspring **inherit** characteristics from their parents is called **genetics**:

- the inheritance of a **single** characteristic is called **monohybrid inheritance**
- paired genes controlling a particular characteristic are called **alleles**
- if the alleles of a pair controlling a characteristic are identical, then the individual is **homozygous** for that characteristic
- if the alleles of a pair controlling a characteristic are different then the individual is **heterozygous** for that characteristic
- an allele which is expressed (produces the characteristic it controls) in preference to the form of the characteristic controlled by the allele's partner is said to be **dominant**; the partner allele is said to be **recessive** and is expressed only in the absence of its dominant partner
- all of the genes of an individual make up its **genotype**
- the characteristics produced as a result of those genes actively expressing themselves form the individual's **phenotype** (e.g. appearance).

The figure on page 86 shows how the height of pea plants is inherited. **Notice** that:

- letters are used to symbolise alleles
- a capital letter is used to symbolise the dominant member of a pair of alleles (**T** = tall)
- a small letter is used to symbolise the recessive member of a pair of alleles (**t** = short)
- the letter used to symbolise the recessive allele is the same letter as that for the dominant allele.

Monohybrid inheritance – continued

How alleles controlling a characteristic (height) pass from one generation to the next

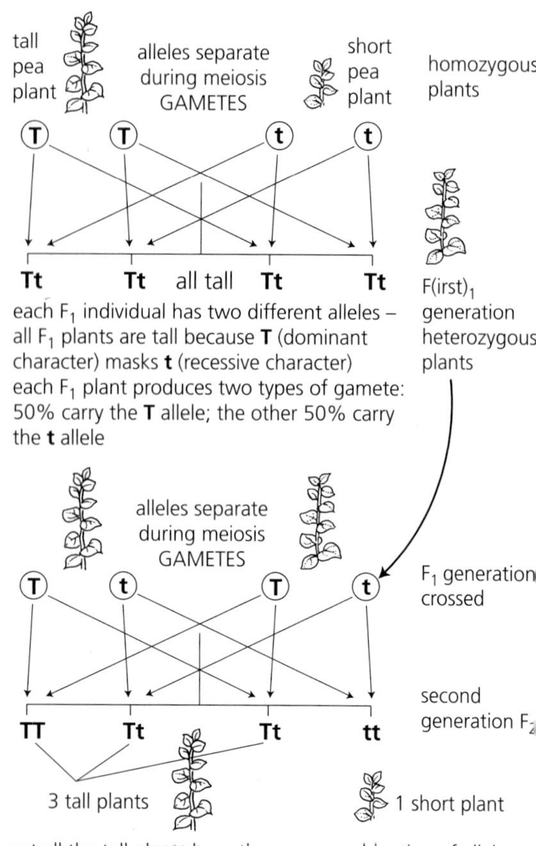

not all the tall plants have the same combination of alleles: 50% are heterozygous – they have both dominant and recessive alleles (**Tt**), 25% of plants are homozygous tall (**TT**) the remaining 25% are homozygous short (**tt**)

 See also • p. 30 **Meiosis**

Inheritance of sex

X and **Y** chromosomes determine the sex of a person. The larger chromosome is the X chromosome; the smaller chromosome is the Y chromosome. The body cells of a woman carry two X chromosomes; those of a man carry an X chromosome and a Y chromosome.

The figure below shows how a person's sex is inherited. **Notice** that:

- a baby's sex depends on whether the egg is fertilised by a sperm carrying an X chromosome or one carrying a Y chromosome
- the birth of (almost) equal numbers of girls and boys is governed by the production of equal numbers of X and Y sperms at meiosis.

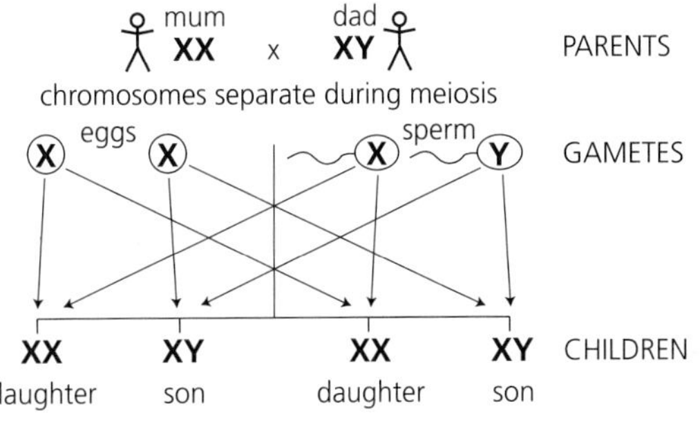

Sex-linked inheritance

Characteristics controlled by alleles situated on the sex chromosomes are said to be sex-linked characteristics. The disease **haemophilia** is an example. The figure below shows what happens.

The outcome when a man affected by haemophilia becomes a father

mum dad

PARENTS

(**Hb** represents the gene for haemophilia: the gene is recessive)

XX x **$X^{Hb}Y$**

chromosomes separate during meiosis

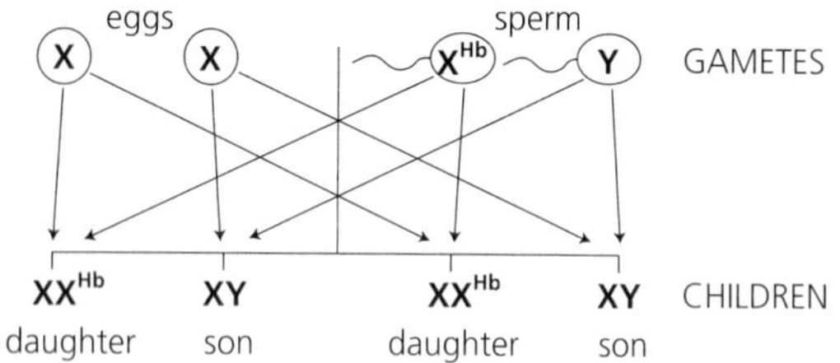

OUTCOME:

the children are not affected by haemophilia but the two daughters are **carriers** of the haemophilia gene

Sex-linked inheritance – continued

The outcome when a woman who is a carrier of the haemophilia allele becomes a mother

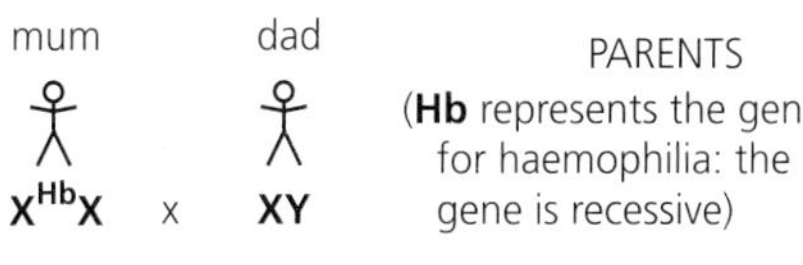

chromosomes separate during meiosis

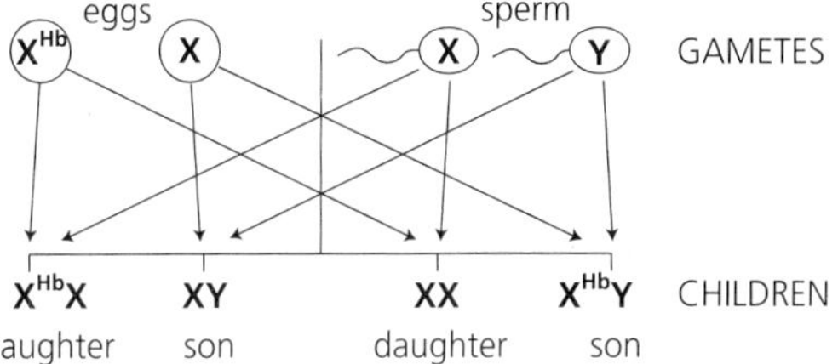

OUTCOME:
one daughter is a **carrier** of the haemophilia gene, one son is affected by haemophilia because the Y chromosome does not carry as many genes as the X chromosome – the recessive haemophilia gene does not have a partner on the Y chromosome to mask its effect.

Genetic engineering

Modern **biotechnology** (the way we use different types of cell to produce useful substances) depends on **genetic engineering**.

- **Restriction enzymes** cut DNA into pieces making it possible to isolate specific genes.
- **Ligase** (splicing enzyme) allows desirable genes to be inserted into the genetic material of host cells.

Using genetic engineering we can create organisms with specific genetic characteristics such that they produce substances that we need and want. The microorganisms are cultured in a solution containing all the substances they require for rapid growth and multiplication inside huge containers called **fermenters**. In this way medicines, foods and industrial chemicals can be made on an industrial scale (see page 91).

- **Batch culture** produces batches of product in a fermenter – the fermenter is then emptied of the product and the nutrient solution and then sterilised with super-heated steam ready for the next batch.
- **Continuous culture** produces substances as an on-going process – the product is drawn off the fermenter and nutrients are replaced as they are used.

Making genetically engineered insulin

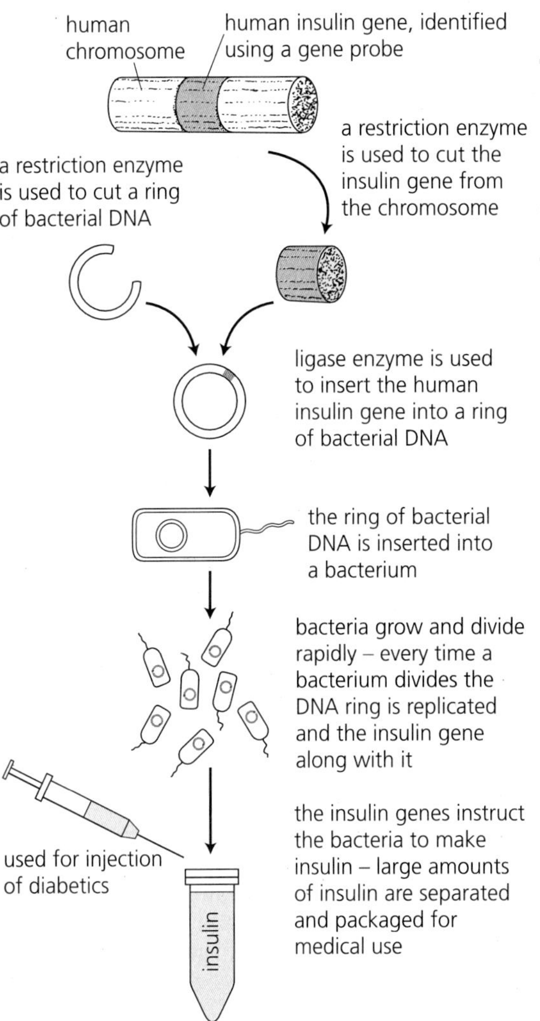
human chromosome
human insulin gene, identified using a gene probe
a restriction enzyme is used to cut the insulin gene from the chromosome
a restriction enzyme is used to cut a ring of bacterial DNA
ligase enzyme is used to insert the human insulin gene into a ring of bacterial DNA
the ring of bacterial DNA is inserted into a bacterium
bacteria grow and divide rapidly – every time a bacterium divides the DNA ring is replicated and the insulin gene along with it
used for injection of diabetics
insulin
the insulin genes instruct the bacteria to make insulin – large amounts of insulin are separated and packaged for medical use

Variation

Differently coloured hair and eyes are examples of the **variations** in the different characteristics which make up an individual's **phenotype**. **Genetic** causes of variation:

- **sexual reproduction** – fertilisation recombines the genetic material from each parent in new ways within the **zygote**
- **mutations** arise as a result of mistakes in the **replication** of DNA – **ionising radiation** and some **chemicals** increase the probability of gene mutation
- **crossing over** during **meiosis** exchanges a segment of one chromosome (and the genes it carries) with the corresponding segment of its homologous chromosome.

Variations that arise from genetic causes are inherited and are the raw material on which **natural selection** acts, resulting in **evolution**. **Environmental** causes of variation:

- **nutrients** in food affect the size of individuals
- **drugs** may have a serious effect on appearance (e.g. **thalidomide**)
- **temperature** affects the rate of enzyme-controlled chemical reactions e.g. warmth increases the rate of photosynthesis
- **physical training** uses the muscles more than normal, increasing their size and power.

Variations that arise from environmental causes are not inherited because the sex cells are not affected. Instead the characteristics are said to be **acquired**. Because variations as a result of acquired characteristics are not inherited, they do not affect evolution.

 See also • p. 85 **Phenotype** • p. 82 **Zygote** • **Rapid Revision Physics, Topic 6,** p. 66 • p. 30 **Meiosis** • p. 94 **Evolution**

Variation – continued

The variations shown by some characteristics are spread over a range of measurements. All intermediate forms of a characteristic are possible between one extreme and the other. We say that the characteristic shows **continuous variation**.

Variation in the height of the adult human population – an example of continuous variation

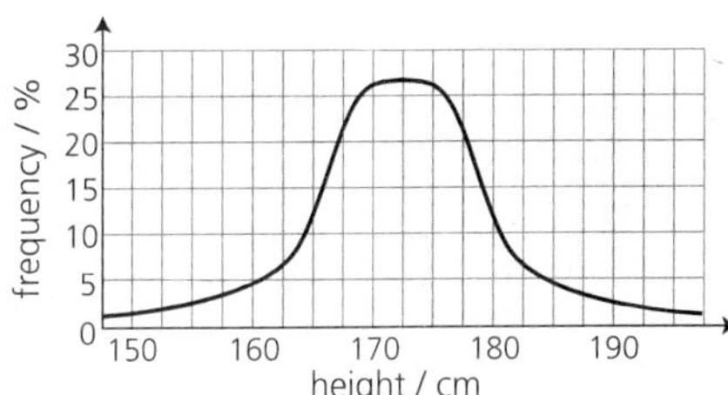

Other characteristics do not show a continuous trend in variation from one extreme to another. They show categories of the characteristic without any intermediate forms. The ability to roll the tongue is an example – you can either do it or you can't. We say that the characteristic shows **discontinuous variation**.

Ability to roll the tongue – an example of discontinuous variation

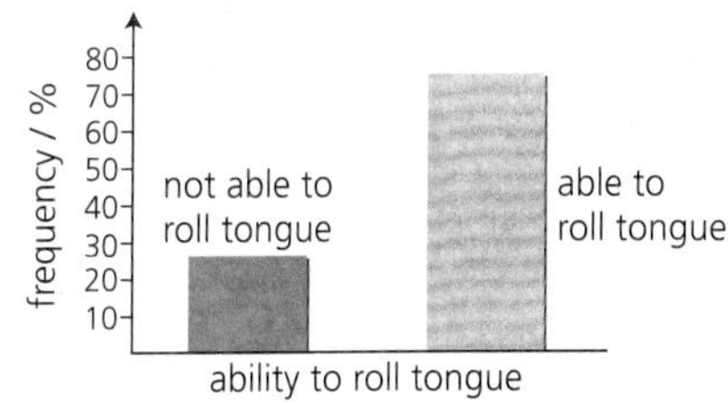

Evolution

Present-day organisms are descended from **ancestors** that have changed through thousands of generations. The process of change is called **evolution**. **Fossils** are the remains of or impressions made by dead organisms. They are **direct** evidence that evolution has taken place.

How species evolve:

- because offspring vary genetically, individuals of the same species are slightly different from one another (except identical twins)
- organisms compete for resources in limited supply; variation means that individuals with genes that express characteristics which suit (**adapt**) the individuals to obtain scarce resources are more likely to survive than other less well adapted individuals; the process is called **natural selection** and is the mechanism of evolution
- the best adapted individuals are more likely to survive and reproduce and so their offspring will inherit the genes for those favoured characteristics
- in this way organisms accumulate genes for favourable characteristics and change through time; that is, they evolve over many generations
- if the environment in which individuals are living changes – then genes for different characteristics might favour survival; individuals with these characteristics will survive to reproduce and so evolution continues from generation to generation.

The figure on page 95 shows an example of evolution in action.

 See also • p. 21 **Population** • p. 9 **Species** • p. 92 **Variation** • p. 20 **Competition** • p. 85 **Gene expression**

Evolution – continued

Different forms of Biston betularia *adapt the moth to survive in different environments*

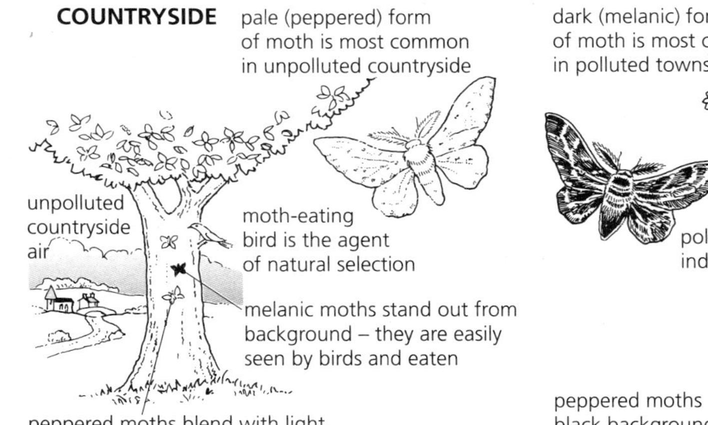

COUNTRYSIDE
pale (peppered) form of moth is most common in unpolluted countryside
unpolluted countryside air
moth-eating bird is the agent of natural selection
melanic moths stand out from background – they are easily seen by birds and eaten
peppered moths blend with light background of lichen-covered tree trunk
TOWN
dark (melanic) form of moth is most common in polluted towns and cities
polluted air in industrial area
moth-eating bird is the agent of natural selection
peppered moths stand out from black background – they are easily seen by birds and eaten
melanic moths blend with soot-covered tree trunk

Inheritance and evolution

Questions

1 Distinguish between the processes of kneading, proving and baking in the making of bread.
2 What are the advantages to diabetics of using insulin produced by bacteria into which the human insulin gene has been inserted?
3 In humans the gene for brown eyes **(B)** is dominant to the gene for blue eyes **(b)**. (a) Using the symbols B and b, state the genotypes of the children that could be born from a marriage between a heterozygous father and a blue-eyed mother. (b) State whether the children are brown-eyed or blue-eyed.
4 Why are acquired characteristics not inherited?
5 Why does sexual reproduction produce much more genetic variation than asexual reproduction?
6 Distinguish between evolution and natural selection.

Answers

1 kneading – repeated folding of the dough makes spaces for carbon dioxide produced by the action of yeast enzymes on the sugar in the dough / proving – carbon dioxide fills the spaces produced by kneading / baking – kills yeast, stopping the action of enzymes / ethanol produced by yeast fermenting sugars is driven off **2** genetically engineered insulin is cheaper; available in large quantities; and chemically the same as human insulin; preventing a possible immune response to injection of the hormone **3** (a) **Bb** or **bb** (b) 50% of the children would be brown-eyed; 50% blue-eyed **4** acquired characteristics are those produced in the individual as a result of the influence (effects) of the environment / these characteristics are not the result of genetic influence and are therefore not inherited **5** during sexual reproduction: genetic material inherited from both parents recombines in the fertilised egg producing combinations of genetic material in the offspring different from the combination in each of the parents / during asexual reproduction: offspring inherit identical genetic material from one parent; mutation is the only source of variation **6** evolution – the change that occurs through many generations of descendants from different ancestors / natural selection – the mechanism of evolution through the survival of favourable variations